PRAISE

THE SUCCESS GROWER

"Mark Schinnerer has identified a truth many never see in a lifetime. True success doesn't just happen. You don't find success. Just like every other natural process on earth, success is something you grow. You plant it, you nurture it and one day you reap the rewards of your work. *The Success Grower* shows you how. A must read."

Ken Davis
International Speaker, Award Winning Comedian
Trainer of Communicators.

"Mark provocatively pulls you into a story of personal success and growth by cultivating the seeds of the dreams we each have kept secretly hidden. Through his story, The Success Grower, you will learn how to plant the seeds of success and reap a harvest you once only dreamed about."

Jeff Brown
Creator & Host, *Read To Lead Podcast.*

"Having grown up on a farm I love being reminded of the lessons we can learn from nature. *The Success Grower* is an intriguing story of how the best business principles can be seen in the simple process of planting, weeding, watering and reaping the harvest. Dreams come to life by using the same proven plan."

Dan Miller
New York Times bestselling author,
48 Days to the Work You Love

"Mark uses his experience of planning, planting, cultivating, nurturing, and harvesting crops as insight into growing dreams and reaching goals. I loved the unique metaphor."

Kary Oberbrunner
Author of *Elixir Project, Day Job To Dream Job The Deeper Path, and Your Secret Name.*

"The pursuit of success for me was paramount; it consumed my every thought. However, much later in life, my quest for significance surpassed that desire many times over. Mark shares ideas and tactics in this book, *The Success Grower: Eight Down-to-Earth Elements For Achieving Your Goals* that will allow you to bypass many of the obstacles that get in the way of a well-lived life. This book will help you achieve the long sought after success that lies just below the surface."

Aaron Walker
President/Founder of View From The Top, Author, *View From The Top.*

"I love the approach Mark Schinnerer takes in THE SUCCESS GROWER: planting someone in crisis in a place where a guide appears and reveals powerful insights that lead them through the crisis is a timeless path to a great story. And that's what this book is—a great story in the tradition of Og Mandino and many others that keeps you engaged and reminds you of the classic success secrets that we all too often lose sight of in our day to day pursuits. Along the way you're forced to acknowledge the way we often ignore that which matters most and recognize the limits that thinking imposes. Read it, apply it, and watch your life change...a big ask for any book, but one this book can and will deliver."

Michael Hudson
Host of the *Get Your Message Heard* podcast

"I love experiential learning, and this book is experiential learning at its best! You'll love this journey of planting, cultivating, and harvesting. And along the way, you'll learn lots about success and significance."

Kent Julian
Professional Speaker and President of *LiveItForward.com*.

"Armed with a picturesque analogy woven beautifully throughout, Schinnerer adeptly ties truth and story together to create this "life manual." Through parable, he reveals pivotal life elements everyone can benefit from in a poignant way so we can actually hear—and hopefully, heed. Easy to read from start to finish, this work will change lives for years to come."

Sarah Beckman
Professional Speaker, Certified Communications Coach
Author, *Alongside*.

THE SUCCESS GROWER

*Eight Down-to-Earth Elements
for Achieving Your Goals*

MARK SCHINNERER

Printed in the United States of America

Published by Author Academy Elite
P.O. Box 43, Powell, OH 43035

www.AuthorAcademyElite.com

Paperback ISBN- 978-1-64085-102-3
Hardcover ISBN- 978-1-64085-103-0

Library of Congress Control Number: 2017912174
Author Academy Elite, Powell, Ohio

Dedicated to
Clyde Schinnerer
– my father –
the most successful
grower I know

"The miracle of the seed and the soil is not available by affirmation; it is only available by labor... The greatest form of maturity is at harvest time. This is when we must learn to reap without complaint if the amounts are small and how to reap without apology if the amounts are big... You must get good at one of two things: sowing in the spring or begging in the fall... The soil says: 'don't bring me your need, bring me your seed.'"

—Jim Rohn

1

The car came out of nowhere.

A sudden flash of red and the morning sunlight reflecting off its windshield were the only warning of an imminent collision. Alan Morris, snapping out of a driver's stupor, instinctively swerved his car to the right and slammed on the brakes.

Skidding on the gravel shoulder of the narrow road, Alan fought for control and slid sideways off the road and down into the ditch. A loud grinding noise followed by a quick jerk, and the sound of metal hitting metal ended his slide.

He had no idea where he was, he had been driving for hours. Sleep had been futile last night. So Alan had gotten up, thrown a few clothes and his toothbrush in a bag, gotten in his car and started driving. No plan, no destination in mind, just drive. He had to get away.

But there was no getting away now. He was stuck in the ditch.

2

At 37, Alan could see his future as Vice President at Jackson Group all laid out for him. After spending his last two summers in college as an intern while finishing up his bachelor's degree in marketing, he accepted a position as a marketing assistant. He immediately enrolled in a Master's program, and after three years, he earned his Master's in Marketing.

Because he was good at developing relationships with prospective customers, he earned several promotions, eventually heading up the New Client Acquisition group in the firm. His real strength lay in studying his clients and their potential markets, so he could better understand the climate they operated in and the issues of demand and supply for their products or services.

By the time he was thirty, he was promoted to Senior Marketing Manager and developed a staff that focused on creativity and innovation as the markets changed. This also included working with their client's PR and sales departments to ensure that the market research they were doing was reliable. This allowed them to create ongoing marketing campaigns that kept their clients at the leading edge of their markets. Alan had then set his sights on becoming Vice President of Marketing Development with the firm.

Over time, as his department continued to grow, Alan became more active, getting into the details of the market research and implementing new marketing strategies for their clients. This was when he began to see a change in the new, younger staff being hired. They no longer seemed to want to spend time 'learning the ropes' as he had done. It was now becoming a more frequent occurrence to butt heads and have strategy sessions end in conflict. The new ideas and concepts they wanted to use had no research to back them up, so Alan felt they were too risky to even put on the table.

After a couple of years trying to get the new staff to understand and follow the business practices that had made the firm successful, he was seeing them more frequently going above him to promote their ideas. His biggest frustration was their insistence they have a 'seat at the table' for the development of new marketing campaigns. This continued to create more conflict, and the division between the long-term staff and the younger, more recently hired group became apparent.

It eventually came to a showdown at a department meeting to discuss the marketing plan for a new bio-technology client. Beverly Ellison, the Division Director and Alan's supervisor, was also at the meeting.

Alan and his team presented their plan for the new marketing campaign. Beverly asked questions about their market research, the customers being targeted by the campaign, and how it would integrate with the new burgeoning bio-tech markets. Alan was prepared for the questions and answered with his research and analysis.

Then Beverly turned to a group of the younger staff and asked their opinion. This sent Alan's blood pressure skyrocketing! Never before had the junior staff been asked for their input. They had always been a supporting part of the team.

Now they were given the opportunity to float their own ideas. They didn't hold back, feeling they had the support of the Division Director, and laid out their own plan for a robust social media campaign that was drastically opposed to the plan Alan had championed. Alan felt he'd been set up, and Beverly had obviously been a part of it. After hearing both proposals, Beverly chose the one from the younger staff.

Alan was livid! After the meeting he asked to speak to Beverly in her office.

"I can't believe you went with their proposal," Alan said, red-faced and barely able to maintain his composure. "I thought it was my responsibility to develop the proposal and submit it for review and approval. When did we decide to turn the meeting into a contest? They're on my team, and I thought they supported the proposal we put together. I didn't know they'd planned a coup!"

Alan paced briskly back and forth across Beverly's office with his fists clenched.

"Calm down, Alan." Beverly put her hand on Alan's shoulder. He just stared at her, choking back words he would only regret saying.

She said, "It's not the end of the world. It just seems the marketing industry is changing and it's good to listen to new ideas. Yes, they came to me earlier and told me how they thought you didn't value their input or their ideas. They just want to be heard, and listened to, and have a chance to develop some new concepts."

"And you bought into it without discussing it with me first?" Alan said incredulously, waving his arms wildly. "I've put in a bunch of years here and have a pretty good track record of successful campaigns. I think I deserved at least a heads up before being bushwhacked!"

He picked up a stack of papers on one of the chairs, threw them on Beverly's desk, and plopped down into a chair.

"Slow down, Alan, let's give it a chance," Beverly said, standing behind him. "Yes, you've done some amazing work here at the firm, and you're one of our rising stars. But I think you're also a bit intimidated by the knowledge and skills of the younger staff, especially when it comes to the new social media marketing. You used to be just as energetic when you first came. Maybe you've forgotten what it's like to be new and excited about the possibilities of creating successful ideas."

"I don't know. I just don't understand not being informed or in the loop on this." Alan held his head in his hands, resting his elbows on his knees. "I'm not very happy about how this went down. I hope they know what they're doing. I'm going to give them their shot. Let's see what they can do. I've got some vacation time coming and I'm going to take it."

Beverly took a deep breath, walked over, and sat on the edge of her desk in front of Alan. She looked him squarely in the eyes.

"If you need some time off, you certainly deserve it. I'm going to let you have a couple of weeks. Take the time to get your mind around this. You're a valuable asset to the firm, and we need to find a way to integrate the younger staff and the changes in the marketing landscape."

"Well, that's just great! Thanks for not supporting me in the meeting, and now you're telling me I need to change the way I run my department and staff." Alan stood and headed for the door. "I'll take the time off and see where my thoughts take me. Since they're getting to run this project,

I'll just be gone. I'll be out of touch until I get back. I'm even shutting off my phone!" Alan waved his phone at Beverly.

He stormed out of her office, slamming the door behind him.

Alan finished the day, cleared up a few open items on his calendar, and left. He wasn't sure what his future was at this point. He felt betrayed and outmaneuvered. He needed a break.

3

Alan's hands were still shaking from the skid into the ditch and the near miss of an accident. "That's just great," he muttered to himself as he tried to restart his car. He turned the key in the ignition, but the only answer he got from the engine was a series of clicks.

"Of course you won't start, you stupid car," he yelled as he slammed his fist on the steering wheel. "Who in the world would be driving down the middle of the road?" He slowly shook his head, wanting to put the blame on anyone but himself. He knew he'd been mindlessly driving, not paying attention to the road.

But now, realizing he wasn't the only one who swerved, he wondered what had happened to the other car.

He forced his door open and stepped into the ditch filled with grass burrs that clung to his jeans like frightened kittens. Slowly, but with a bit of concern, he climbed out of the ditch to the top of the road.

"Hey buddy, are you okay?" someone called out. Running down the road toward Alan was a guy in a white polo shirt and blue shorts.

"Man, you sure gave me a scare! I came over the hill and there you were on the wrong side of the road. Are you all right?" the man said, his hands trembling.

"Yeah, I'm fine. Sorry about that, my mind was somewhere else," Alan said, embarrassed. "And you?"

"Yep, I'm good. Just glad you're okay. I'm Tony, and you are...?"

"Alan. Alan Morris," he replied, extending his hand. "I'm sorry to give you a scare. I think my car is broken, won't start."

Shaking hands, Tony said, "Well, let's see what we can do to get you out of the ditch, and then we'll get you to town and have Buddy at the repair shop look at your car. You can grab some coffee and something to eat if you want, at the Sunrise Café. They've got the best coffee and cinnamon rolls around."

"Thanks," Alan said as they walked back to Tony's car.

After calling for a tow truck and watching Alan's car being pulled from the ditch, they followed the truck to the repair shop.

While Buddy was getting Alan's car pushed into the work bay, Alan thanked Tony and apologized again for the frightening encounter on the road. Afterwards, Alan started walking the two blocks to the Sunrise Café. A strong cup of hot coffee would be a comforting companion right now.

The little bell hanging above the café's door jingled to announce his arrival. Inside, a red counter trimmed in aluminum ran along the right side of the café, iconic round silver stools with red vinyl seats were bolted to the floor along the counter. On the opposite wall stood a row of red vinyl booths with the same table as the counter.

Four of the six stools were already taken and the booths were all occupied with the breakfast crowd of locals, obviously regulars, who were bantering back and forth with each other about last fall's high school football team. Monday morning quarterbacking had never been more opinionated.

Alan chose to sit at the far end of the counter. The waitress came over and asked, "Whatcha havin'?"

Alan looked at her name tag and saw her name was Evelyn. "I'll just have some coffee, black, and one of your famous cinnamon rolls."

"Oh, you're new in town and already heard about them, huh? So who was it, Fred or Tony? They tell everyone they meet about our 'famous' cinnamon rolls!"

"It was Tony, met him by accident, actually," Alan replied with a slight chuckle.

"All right, coffee and a roll it is. It'll never be better than today," she said as she poured him a cup of steaming coffee.

He figured she was talking about the cinnamon roll but thought today had started off pretty rough—surely it had to get better.

The little bell above the door jingled again. Glancing at the mirror behind the counter, Alan saw an older man in bib overalls and a sweat-stained John Deere cap walk through the door.

A chorus of "Morning, Tom!" rippled through the café as the old man made his way to the counter and took the stool next to Alan, the only seat left in the place.

Evelyn brought Alan a plate with the biggest cinnamon roll he had ever seen. A smear of butter was melting and slowly coating the top, pooling in the swirls. He had never had butter on a cinnamon roll before but thought he should just go with it.

"I see Evelyn talked you into the cinnamon roll," Tom said as he poured two spoonful's of sugar into his coffee, stirring it with the spoon.

"It'll never be better than today."

"Yeah, that's what she said," Alan replied, nodding toward Evelyn, not really wanting to have a conversation.

Evelyn returned and slid a plate of bacon, eggs, and toast in front of the old man.

"Morning, Tom. How grows the farm today?" she asked.

"Some days are better and some days just get better."

"Well, just keep 'em growing out there!" she replied.

From the sound of it, this was their usual morning greeting, and now Alan knew the old man was a farmer. He should have guessed from the dried mud on the old man's boots and the dirty cap.

The cinnamon roll with the melted butter oozing across the top was an amazing treat. It melted in your mouth, the butter adding just a touch of saltiness to the sweet sticky roll.

Alan now understood that the experience of eating one for the first time could never be had again.

"See, I told you. It'll never be better than today. Your first experience always makes the biggest impression," Tom said.

"Yeah, this is actually amazing! It's the best cinnamon roll I've ever had!"

"So what brings you to our little town?" Tom asked as he used the last corner of his toast to mop up the last of the egg yolk on his plate.

"Oh, I had a little trouble on the road so my car is in the repair shop down the street."

"Where are you headed to so early in the morning out in the middle of nowhere?"

"I'm just passing through. Took some time off from work, don't have a plan to go anywhere, just thought I'd drive and get away for a while," Alan answered.

"Hmm, just want to get away, huh? Get away from what?" the old man prodded.

Alan was pretty sure Tom wouldn't understand the frustration and pressure he was under at work to not only produce but to keep up with the new, younger staff. They wanted to be in charge without having the experience, and they wasted so much of their time on their smartphones and called it networking.

Now it looked like his future as a VP was in jeopardy because the company was changing tactics and practices to cater to them. To top it off, his boss just gave them the lead on his most recent project without discussing it with him first. It was like all his experience and time with the company were being thrown away or weren't valued. He now wondered if he was becoming obsolete—at 37!

"Well, it's complicated, and with the way things are changing with these younger kids working today, it's frustrating and irritating. I just needed to take some time and clear my head," Alan explained vaguely.

"And no plan for where you're going. How will you know when you get there?"

"Nope, no plan. Just driving where the road takes me. I guess that's here for now," Alan said, sliding his plate across the counter.

"Well, I find that I'll never have a successful harvest if I don't have a plan first," Tom said. "And I don't make those plans one year at a time. I have to think about how the crops affect the soil and if it needs to rest for a time. Does it need fertilizer, and how much water does it need? Nope, you certainly can't have a harvest without a plan."

Alan rolled his eyes. He really didn't want an explanation about farming. All he wanted to do was get away and not think about it.

"I find life to be the same way," Tom continued. "If we don't take the time to plan our future—where we're headed, what our goals are, what knowledge and skills we need—and have a structure to accomplish it, well, we pretty much end up with a mess. If you don't have a plan to get where and what you want in life, then you shouldn't be upset with what you get."

The bell on the door to the café jingled again, and Buddy the mechanic walked in.

Good, Alan thought to himself. His car was fixed and he could get on down the road. He really didn't want to continue this conversation. It was making him a bit uncomfortable for some reason.

"Hey there, Mr. Morris," Buddy said as he walked to the end of the counter. "Gotcha all checked out and it's not good news."

Alan felt a sickening knot balling up in his stomach. "Yeah, that's how my day started. Just tell me."

"Well, when you slid across that culvert it punched a hole in your oil pan and cracked the housing to the transmission. I can fix it, but it will take several days to get the parts here, being how it's a foreign-made car, and a week or so to get it all fixed."

Alan felt like he'd been punched in the stomach. He wondered if his day could get any worse.

"Are you sure you can fix it?" Alan asked. "Maybe I should have it towed to another town with a dealership that might have the parts and mechanics who know how to work on it—no disrespect, Buddy."

"Naw, I understand, but I used to work in one of those big shops on these cars. I just moved out here because things were simpler and I could grow my own business. Besides, the closest one is over 250 miles away. Don't worry, Mr. Morris, I'll take good care of her and she'll be as good as new when I'm done," Buddy said with a confidence that gave Alan some comfort.

"Okay, thanks. I'll be down in a minute," Alan replied, realizing he was going to be spending a while here.

Alan just wanted to kick himself for being so stupid and driving all night, angry and irritated, and more wrapped up in his mind than paying attention to the road. Now he was stuck in this little town, and fixing his car was going to be expensive.

He certainly had the time. He had already scheduled to take some time off. He just hadn't planned on spending it in the middle of nowhere.

"So, you're going to be here a while, huh?" Tom said as he swirled more sugar into his coffee.

"It sure looks like it. It's not what I had planned on, but I guess I really didn't have a plan," Alan said, and immediately regretted saying it because he was probably going to get another lesson in farming.

"Well, you need one now," said Tom. "I'll tell you what, let me give you a ride to Buddy's so you can make arrangements with him about your car. Then come on out to my place. It's only a few miles out of town. You can stay there. There's no motel or anything here. It'll be nice to have the company since it's just me out there."

"Oh, I'd hate to impose. I'd just be in your way."

"Not at all. It's a big house and you can just hang out if you want. I've got quite a bit to do now that summer's here. The crops are beginning to grow, so I've got to get back to work."

"I guess I don't have another option, thanks," Alan replied with a sigh.

After squaring things with Buddy to get the parts ordered and approve the repairs to his car, Alan grabbed his bag with the few clothes he had thrown in and climbed into Tom's old faded red Ford pickup. They headed out of town. Alan had never been on a farm before and was pretty sure these were going to be some of the longest boring days he'd ever had.

"So, you ever been on a farm?" Tom asked.

"Nope, first time," Alan replied hesitantly.

"Well, it's pretty quiet out here and you get a lot of time to think and make plans. In fact, that's what's great about the winter. You have some down time to look at the past year, the crops you grew, the ones that did great, the ones that needed some cultivating, and the ones that didn't work out so well," Tom said as he drove.

"Each year is different and each season is different. If I don't spend some time reviewing the successes and failures, and the reasons for them, then I risk having more failures. Most of the time it's a cause related to the soil. Not enough moisture or too much, it needs fertilizer, or it has been put into production too long and needs a rest."

"I had no idea farming was that involved," Alan said. "I just thought you planted the seed in the ground, gave it some water, and it grew."

"Yeah, I get that a lot from you city guys." Tom chuckled. "When you get right down to it, it's not much different than planning for success in anything else in life."

Alan sat there quietly, thinking there was no way farming could compare with the fast-paced world of marketing and business where every day you had to make million-dollar decisions that could make or break the company. And then there were all the employees you had to deal with, which made the job even harder. He wondered if Tom even had one employee. He was pretty sure he didn't have a clue what it was like to work with hundreds.

4

The pickup truck slowed and turned left off the road onto a tree-lined drive. The trees were filled with leaves that made a canopy completely covering the drive. Morning light filtered through the leaves, casting an emerald-green glow on the road as they drove through the tunnel of trees.

The house was an old but stately, two-story house with a huge wrap-around porch on the front, one side facing the road. The yard was filled with large trees, and the grass, beginning to green up for the summer, was as thick as an old plush shag carpet.

As they drove around to the back, Alan saw there was a shop building with an old red-and-white tractor sitting next to it. There were other pieces of equipment sitting in a row behind the tractor, but he had no idea what there were or what they did.

Tom pulled around and parked in the back of the big house, right next to an old and beautiful black Mercedes Benz 380SL.

"Oh my gosh!" Alan exclaimed with shocked amazement. He pointed at the Mercedes. "Where did you get that?"

"Oh, that? I've had it for a long time," Tom replied as if it were no big deal. "I like to keep it cleaned up and looking good and running good."

"That's sweet! What year is it?" Alan asked excitedly.

"1985, isn't she a beauty?"

"Oh man, you just don't see those every day! I never expected to see one way out here. How long have you had it?"

"Since 1985. It's a reminder of days past." Tom's voice trailed off with the memory.

Alan wondered what that past might have been to have that car. Here he was, an old farmer driving a faded red pickup, with an old Mercedes parked in the drive that he kept looking shiny new.

"I'll show you where you can put your things," Tom said, snapping back to the present. "You can help yourself to the fridge and whatever else you can find in the kitchen. There's plenty to eat, so don't worry about it. My place is your place."

"Thanks," Alan said as he followed Tom into the house. "I won't be much of a bother. I took some time off from work and I told them I'd be out of touch for a while. I guess I'll just take advantage of the quiet time."

"Sure thing, whatever you need. I've got work to do so make yourself at home," Tom said as he pointed to a bedroom adjacent to the dining room. "Come on outside later, and I'll give you the nickel tour of the place."

The bedroom was small, most of it taken up by the bed. A dresser was shoved into one corner, and across from it, a small rocking chair with a split wooden seat. There was a window at the side of the room that looked out toward the road. Alan tossed his bag on the bed and wandered around the house.

For an old man living alone, the house was surprisingly clean and orderly, Alan thought. He'd expected to see the normal signs of 'nesting' and accumulation of the stuff we all bring into our lives to make us comfortable. But this place felt different. Not in a creepy or weird way, but almost inviting. It was as if Tom knew he would have company today.

The living room had some very nice leather furniture arranged with the television as the focal point. A well-used recliner was set in the corner with a stand and lamp next to it. There were a couple of books on the stand, the top one being a bible, Alan noticed. Glancing at the other book, he saw it was one by Dale Carnegie on effective speaking. *That's odd*, he thought with a chuckle to himself, *why would an old farmer be reading about public speaking?*

Alan had never been on a farm nor had he given much thought to how crops grow or where the food he ate actually came from. Growing up in the city, there wasn't much exposure to this way of life, and with the constant rush of people and traffic, you mostly learn to shut it out and go with the flow.

Now, it was quiet. He had never before experienced a silence like this. It was almost deafening. Alan was certain the next couple of weeks was going to drive him crazy and bore him to death.

To keep from going stir crazy, Alan decided to try and make the best of it. He went outside to look around the place and find Tom to see if he could lend a hand.

He found Tom busy working on some piece of equipment that looked like it had hundreds of curved spines on multiple rotating wheels.

"Wow, what's this crazy-looking thing used for?" Alan asked, pointing to the machine.

Tom, who was busy with a wrench, looked up. "Oh, this? It's a cultivator. When you run it through the field, it tills the soil in between your crop rows to clean up any weeds and allow the air and moisture to get into the soil better. Weeds are always around, and if you don't deal with them early they tend to take over." He asked, "Have you ever been in a corn field?

"No, I've never been on a farm before," Alan replied.

"Okay, let's walk out into the field and I'll show you."

Tom got up from under the cultivator, and they walked across the yard to the field next to the house. He waded into a sea of green that was swaying a bit in the morning breeze. The corn was a couple of feet tall, with thick stalks and long, wide leaves.

Tom stopped, knelt down between the rows, and motioned for Alan to join him. He started scratching the dirt.

"You see here, the rains that we've had and the drying sun and wind have crusted over the soil, making it hard for more rain and air to get into the ground well. And you can see the weeds that have grown up in between the rows. When you look out over the field, you can't see any weeds, but when you get down and look up close, there they are. It might look fine on the outside, but they'll grow bigger and become a nuisance, or even take over if they aren't dealt with."

Tom looked off across the waves of stalks.

"It's kind of like our lives," he continued, "we go to school, start our lives and careers thinking if we just work hard, keep our heads down and follow the corporate path, we'll advance and maybe get a big promotion.

"But then it gets hard. Rules change, markets change, the economy changes, and people with new ideas come along. If we haven't been paying attention and adding to our knowledge and skills, we find ourselves getting cynical and resentful and frustrated. It affects our attitudes and our production. Over time, we end up feeling as if we missed an opportunity or that there's more we should be doing, but we've become comfortable in our situation and can't see a way out. That's how the weeds in our life take over. We become hardened in our attitude, just like this soil and the field."

Alan knelt there, amazed at Tom's comparison of growing corn and working in a job, and the course lives take. How could he know what working for a big company was like and its challenges? How would he know about the demands and struggles to produce and grow a business, attracting new customers and staying at the cutting edge of technology just to keep up with the competition? But his comparison did make a bit of sense. He had found himself frustrated and resentful, especially with the pressure he felt from the younger generation coming into the workforce. His plan to advance and become a VP was being threatened, and he was feeling that now he might have missed his opportunity. Oddly, he did have a gnawing sense he was supposed to be doing something greater or different, but he didn't know if it was just boredom with his current situation or something bigger.

"So how do you keep the weeds out?" Alan asked, a bit more interested.

"Oh, you can't keep them out." Tom brushed aside the corn leaves. "You find a way to control them. Weeds are always looking for an opportunity; they're always waiting on the right conditions to grow. They need moisture and air like all plants, and they need soil to grow in. They especially can grow in the worst soil because nothing else will grow there. There are weeds that when young look a lot like the plants you want to grow. If you don't deal with them early on, then you'll be dealing with them at harvest time, and you'll end up mixing the weed seeds in with the good seeds, creating an even bigger problem next season."

This farm lesson was getting a bit lost on Alan. He scrunched up his forehead. Tom, who seemed to notice his confusion, grabbed a weed, tugging on it a bit to loosen the soil, and pulled it up to reveal the long spreading roots. He then explained.

"You see how determined the weeds are to take hold and grow? Look at how long this tap root is and the supporting roots around the base of the weed." Tom shook the dirt from the roots. "If you let them get firmly rooted, it gets harder and harder to control them and get rid of them. Dealing with them when they're still small is better. They'll always be there, but it's our responsibility to control them and work on growing the successful, healthy crop that then takes up the empty space and overshadows the weeds."

Alan was becoming more curious. He pulled up a weed of his own.

"That's how life is," Tom said, tossing the weed on the ground. "We start out with great hopes and plans and dreams for our lives. Eventually, little things start taking more of our time. The daily grind to produce at work, support our families, and meet our obligations, while thinking it will advance our opportunities, all start to wear us down. We get so tied up in our daily lives we forget about the dreams and plans we had when we started out. We're so focused on the 'stuff' in our lives we start to resent it and feel like we aren't achieving what we were meant to achieve. We get more frustrated and face more pressures at work to keep up with everything that's changing, and it's all we can do just to survive. Every day becomes a grind, and we wish we could find a way out. We want to do something different, but we don't know what it is or how to get there.

We feel stuck. That's when we're living in a field of weeds instead of a field that's growing toward a harvest."

"Yeah, that's right," Alan heard himself say out loud as he sat down on the ground between the rows of corn.

He was feeling stuck, as if everything in his life was choking him. He could see how the 'weeds' in life slowly creep in and take hold. He certainly was frustrated he wasn't achieving the position or success he had wanted. Maybe he didn't pay enough attention to the details. As long as he did what he was told and worked hard and produced, he thought he would reach his goal. Now he considered that maybe he should have developed a plan, should had been more in control of the path he was pursuing to reach his goal. He had let others determine his future. Had he allowed them to plant their weeds in his field, and now he was just letting them grow? The thought made his chest tighten.

"This morning at the café, you said that you can't have a harvest without a plan." Alan looked up at Tom. "How do you plan for all the things that can happen? There's not just the weeds to deal with, but you said that plants need moisture and fertilizer, and something about resting the soil. And I'm guessing the weather isn't always nice like today."

"Well, you were listening this morning, huh?" Tom chuckled, slapping Alan on the leg.

"I'll tell you what. If you really want to learn how to have a successful harvest—even in your own life—let's talk about it this evening after dinner. I've got to get to working on this field. You can just hang around and see how it works or do your own thing. We'll talk tonight."

With that, Tom got up, brushed the dirt off his overalls, and walked back to the tractor. He started it up and headed off into the corn field with his cultivator.

Alan watched Tom drive off into the corn with the dust boiling up behind him. He was somewhat intrigued by what

Tom had said, relating growing crops and farming to how our lives are affected by the influences around us and how we need a plan to be successful. He thought the only plan he needed was to work hard, be dedicated, follow the rules, and consequently, he would be rewarded. But now he sensed that he had missed something.

That evening, as they were eating dinner, Tom said, "So Alan, tell me your story. What brought you to our little corner of the world?"

Alan sat his glass of tea down and leaned back in his chair.

"Well, I grew up in a city of about 50,000 people. My dad is an accountant and works for a small CPA firm, and my mom was a school teacher. I have two sisters who are younger than me. After I graduated from high school I went off to college, determined not to go back home, and got a degree in marketing. I had big expectations of getting a job at a marketing firm and having my own accounts to work. I realized it would be hard for someone to hire me for that kind of position without experience. I was sure I could do it, but eventually, I needed a job. I decided to look for a summer intern position and took the first one I could find just to get started.

"That went well, so I went on to get a Master's degree. After a few years I was promoted to a marketing assistant, handling the marketing for several big national companies along with a bunch of local businesses. I was pretty successful with the clients I had, and received a few awards and recognition for some of the major marketing campaigns I had developed."

Tom leaned forward with his elbows on the table, showing interest in Alan's story.

Alan continued, "That's when I set my sight on a VP spot in the company and kept doing my work. But it seemed the more I took on and the harder I worked, there never was an opportunity to move up. I started to get frustrated with the work and even started looking around for another job. I even thought I could run my own successful firm, but I was making good money where I was.

"So, I was stuck, I thought. After a while, I realized the firm had been hiring some new, younger employees. They were always pushing new ideas and questioning the reasons for the processes we had in place for client acquisition and management as well as our marketing strategies. They were always talking about online marketing and digital media. And the most irritating of all, they were constantly on their phones." Alan waved his arms up in frustration. "They said it was how they stayed connected to the world or markets or something. I didn't get it, or them, and they were always questioning the way we did business.

"The breaking point for me happened in a meeting yesterday, with a bunch of us who'd been working on a new national campaign for a major healthcare client in the bio-technology market I'd recently signed. We had a heated debate, not about the theme or content, but about the structure of the roll-out. The younger guys wanted to try only a social media campaign. They said they could target a specific audience, but I felt that was risky and left out too many people. They kept asking why I thought that, and then they went to the director of our division behind my back who decided she wanted to give it a shot. With a new account!" Alan slapped the table. He didn't realize he was shouting.

After taking a minute to calm himself, he resumed his story. "I was floored by the decision, and I let her know how stupid I thought it was. After a heated conversation, I told her to let the kids take it and see what they could do, even though I didn't agree. I told her I needed some time off—I had two weeks coming, anyway, so I said I was going to take it. And then I ended up in a ditch."

Alan collapsed back in the chair. He was glad to get that out. His frustration with his commitment to his job and the firm, and then not having the support of the director, really made him question his future. Had he not been paying attention to the new way of doing things? He always worked hard, followed the rules, and had been successful. Now he was being challenged by new concepts and new employees who didn't seem to care about following the rules. They wanted to be in charge, it seemed, without putting in the time or having the experience.

After dinner and the dishes were washed, Tom poured them both a glass of iced tea and headed off into the living room. Alan took a seat on the couch across the room from Tom.

"Alan, let me ask you something," Tom began after several minutes of silence.

"You said your goal is to become the vice president in your firm. What have you done to make sure you're ready for that kind of responsibility?"

"Well, I've worked there for several years, taking on all the projects they've given me, brought in new clients, and had a lot of successful campaigns that helped give the firm more visibility in the market," Alan responded.

"Ah, so you were a good soldier, did what you were told, had some good ideas that worked, and you thought that as long as you kept doing that, you'd be rewarded with a VP position. Is that about right?" Tom asked pointedly.

That was pretty blunt, Alan thought, crossing his arms. What would he know about working in a business with bosses you are trying to please and doing what it takes to get recognized and a promotion? How would an old farmer understand?

"Well, that's a pretty simplistic way to put it," Alan shot back. "There's more to it than that."

"Oh, yes, there are the new guys you talked about," Tom said sarcastically. "The younger ones who don't want to follow the 'rules' as you said, and who want to have a say in the project or the process. But you put in your time following the 'rules' so you think they should too. You think they should put in the time to learn how the business works, like you did.

"You're not happy they spend so much time on their little smartphones and walk around with the things in their ears. And now they have caught the attention of the bosses who are giving their new ideas a chance when it took you several years to get your shot at having your ideas put into a project. Does that about get to the rest of it?"

Tom's words stung a bit, hitting a nerve. Alan pouted. He struggled with his emotions, feeling like his life has been suddenly interrupted by circumstances and people outside of his control. He knew what Tom was trying to tell him—in order to accomplish a change in his life, he first needed to confront his feelings and attitude. But it was easier said than done, and he needed to find a way to move forward.

"Yeah, well, I just need to figure out what I'm going to do from here," Alan responded dejectedly.

"That's why I took the vacation I had coming and left them to deal with their new plan."

"So, what's your plan?" Tom asked.

"I don't know yet. I thought some time away would help clear my mind and give me some clarity on what I should do."

"No plan, huh?" Tom kicked back the recliner. "Seems that's how you ended up in the ditch in the first place. You didn't have a plan. So how's that working out for you?"

5

Alan clenched his teeth at Tom's directness, which felt like making light of his situation.

"We were talking this morning about the soil and how to have a successful harvest, not just on the farm but in our lives too," Tom went on as he pushed farther back in his chair. "You've reached a crossroad in your life and the world's changing. Now you don't know what to do because you don't have a plan. So let's change that." He slapped his hands on his knees. "Alan, are you willing to work to reach the success you really want in life? Just letting life happen isn't the way to do it."

Alan sat quietly for a bit, thinking about his life so far and how he'd done everything that was asked of him. He was beginning to realize he was following someone else's plan, not his.

"Sure," Alan said a little reluctantly. "What do I have to lose?"

"Well, that wasn't the attitude I was hoping for, but we can work with it." Tom got up from his chair, walked across the room, and opened a door to what appeared to be an office.

Alan could see a small desk covered with books and papers, and an old wooden chair. A bookcase lined the far wall, filled with books—not neatly arranged but shoved into every available space there was.

At the corner of the bookcase, a portion of the end wall appeared to have several plaques hanging on it, some with little gavels, the kind one would get for chairing a board or committee.

That's a bit odd, Alan thought. Why would an old farmer have all those plaques? Maybe he chaired the local 4H or some farming club.

Tom came out of the office holding what looked like a well-worn leather binder, closed the door, and returned to his chair.

"Alan," he began, "over my lifetime I've seen many changes in business, markets, people, and the economy. I've seen people struggle with their lives and fortunes, and some have been more successful than others. To be clear, success isn't always about money. It's about achieving the goals and things you want in life. But to do that you must understand the way of success.

"At first it was a mystery to me, but then I began to notice that people who achieved their goals and dreams understood something very elemental that only a few would actually follow. The ones who did pretty much had success guaranteed, but not immediately, and many times it was after a lot of failures. But it did come.

"I began to implement these elements in my life and have achieved more success than I dreamed about as a kid. I had gained the recognition of many of my peers who were great leaders in their own companies, and I've had the opportunity to sit in the presence of very powerful and influential men, and helped lead them to even greater success."

"Wait," Alan said, holding up his hand. "I thought you were just a farmer! What business? And if you had that kind of success and influence, why are you a farmer now?"

Tom sighed loudly. "I was in the insurance business, started right out of high school as a file clerk for a large firm. Over time, I took the tests and got licensed, and began selling life insurance. I loved it because I was able to help solve problems for families and give them some security. I always took the time to get to know them and learn about their dreams and wishes, and found ways to help them get there.

"I learned from very successful insurance salesmen and eventually started my own firm. I began studying the most successful businessmen, reading books like *Think and Grow Rich* by Napoleon Hill[1], *As a Man Thinketh* by James Allen[2], and *How to Win Friends and Influence People* by Dale Carnegie[3]. I then implemented everything they taught.

"Eventually, as I developed the elements of success, I started to share what I learned with the top performers in my firm, helping them to reach unimagined success and recognition. Then I decided to share these elements with other business leaders who also saw dramatic increases in business and personal success. But my wife got sick with cancer, and after a tough six months, she died."

"Oh man, I'm sorry to hear that," Alan said, his tone full of sympathy.

Tom waved a hand in acknowledgement. "I began to think about when I was growing up on a farm and how these elements tied directly to the processes and methods of successful farming…and I realized they were universal elements that have existed for thousands of years. We all get so caught up in pursuing success and making our own success that we forget there are specific elements to grow our own success.

"I gave it all up, sold my business, and bought this farm. Now I pass these elements on to people like you who have arrived at a crossroad in their life and are searching for answers. I believe you ended up here for a reason."

"Well, I guess that explains the Mercedes," Alan said, grinning.

"Yeah, it was the dream car. I couldn't let it go." Tom smiled.

Alan stared at the man before him, his awe and wonder leading to increased respect. Maybe Tom was right—he was here for a reason. He sat quietly, patiently waiting for Tom to go on.

"So," Tom said, looking intently at Alan, "before I give you the first element, I need to know if you're willing to commit to follow them. You'll need to give me the two weeks you have, and I need your agreement to do everything I ask you to do. No questions, just trust that following and understanding the elements will lead to greater success in your life. They'll work in business and in your personal life. Do I have your agreement?"

"Well, since I can't go anywhere and don't have anything else to do, yes," Alan said jokingly, thinking it couldn't be too difficult.

"I was hoping for a bit more sincere commitment," Tom said with a touch of sarcasm. He pulled an envelope from the binder and handed it to Alan. It was sealed. On the front was written, 'The Success Grower – Element One.' Tom instructed Alan to open the envelope, read the first element three times before he went to bed tonight and three times again in the morning as soon as he awoke. After that, he was to read it first thing in the morning and again before going to sleep at night.

In the morning, Tom would give him his first instructions for the day.

The Success Grower - Element One
Fertile Soil - Fertile Mind

The soil is alive. It is a living, active organism. It has the potential to yield 10-, 30-, or 100-fold, but only if it is fertile. Care and diligence are required to ensure the soil stays alive. With neglect, it becomes a hard, lifeless wasteland that holds no value. Good soil takes frequent tilling and the addition of nutrients and organic matter that feeds the life-giving structure within the soil to have the energy it needs for productivity.

The mind is like the soil. It is alive, a living and active organism. Like the soil, the mind has a limitless potential for ever-increasing productivity. Care and nurturing are required. It must be fed new knowledge and insights in order for it to grow. If it is neglected and left to its own desires, it becomes a wasteland and produces very little of worth, which some call mediocrity.

You will till the soil of your mind. It must be open and receptive to new ideas. It must be ready to learn. You will look for new opportunities for growth and make it an environment for learning. You will feed it regularly with new wisdom, insights, and knowledge. You will plant in it life-giving ideas and concepts, and water them with reflection, quiet contemplation, and belief. It is belief in yourself that unleashes your potential.

Just like the soil, you will regularly take a season of rest to let your mind regenerate. Soil without a season of rest begins to yield less and less. The mind, without rest, is too filled up with all the ideas, activities, and projects that have come before.

Rest is good for the soil, rest is good for the mind, and rest is good for the soul.

After a season of rest, it yields 1,000-fold.

6

Alan was awakened by the smell of coffee and bacon. It had been a pretty rough night, tossing and turning in bed, his mind churning on the idea of the soil being alive and how it is our decision on what we plant or let grow in it.

He had read the first element three times before he went to bed and was now aware of his mind working over what he had put into it. He had never realized it before now.

Alan sat up groggily on the edge of the bed, his feet resting on the cool wooden floor, and took the First Element. He read it again, three times.

"Well, good morning!" Tom said with a cheery smile, peering over the top of the morning paper as Alan slowly trudged into the kitchen. "It's about time you rolled out for the day. We start pretty early around here. I've got some bacon and eggs on the stove for you, help yourself."

"Coffee, I definitely need the coffee," Alan mumbled.

Tom gently folded the paper and laid it on the table. "Did you do as instructed?" He asked in the tone of a teacher, catching Alan by surprise.

"Yes, I did. Last night and this morning, three times each."

"Wonderful! Today will be the beginning of a new path in your life. You'll begin to see your life and your future in a whole different way. It's not going to be easy, here or the rest of your life, but you'll understand how to plan for, nurture, and harvest personal success. So let's get started. Meet me back out in the corn field. Your first lesson begins this morning."

Tom finished his coffee, put on his broad-brimmed straw hat, and headed out the door.

Alan still wasn't sure how farming could teach anything about the corporate world and personal success. But after spending the night thinking about how the soil and the mind are the same, needing to be a fertile ground for things to grow, he was getting a sense the old man had something to teach him.

Finishing his breakfast, Alan cleaned up and went out looking for Tom in the corn field.

"Welcome to your first lesson. But those tennis shoes are going to be a problem for you." Tom pointed to Alan's shoes. "Are you okay getting them dirty? Because you'll find them filled with dirt after today."

Alan looked at his shoes and at Tom's well-worn work boots. "Yeah, it'll be all right."

"Well, we'll head into town later today and run by Farm Supply to get you a pair of good work boots and a hat. The sun out here'll rip your hide off."

"Okay, thanks." Alan was now wondering what he'd agreed to.

"All right, look back down here," Tom said, pointing at the ground. "Yesterday, this soil was pretty hard and packed, and the weeds were taking hold. Now, after running the cultivator, you can see the soil is nice and loose so the moisture and oxygen can get into the ground better. It also got a lot of the weeds out. But some of them are growing close to the row of corn, or in the corn, and will eventually be a problem.

"Just as in our own lives, we need to keep our mind open and cultivate it so we can accept new information, knowledge, and insights. If we don't keep challenging our minds and putting in good stuff, we become stuck in our thinking. We won't be able to see the new opportunities that come along to help us grow. Eventually, the world passes us by because we haven't continued to feed our minds and develop a mindset of growth. The mindset you have is a choice you get to make."

Alan nodded as he kicked at the dirt.

"Since I'm not going to let you drive the tractor—yet—I have a simpler option that'll help you learn what it's like to till the soil," Tom said with a big grin.

Tom had been using a garden hoe to get some of the weeds that had been left near the corn. Alan now figured it was his turn. He had never used one but knew it was not going to be fun.

"This hoe is a handheld cultivator!" Tom exclaimed. "It's been used for hundreds of years and works just as well today. And you are the lucky fellow that gets to follow in the footsteps of every farmer and gardener, and get up close and personal with the soil."

Tom handed the hoe to Alan—who took it hesitantly—and explained, "Just walk down between two rows of corn and look for weeds on both sides. Find one, give it a good chop, but don't cut down the corn. Whether its corn or your mind, you have to know what to leave in and what to take out. Sometimes it's difficult to get through the packed soil because we'd let it go for so long. We'd become set in our ways."

Alan took the hoe, gently chopped at a small weed, and looked up to the far end of the row. It looked like it was a mile away.

"How long is this row?" Alan asked, now regretting his commitment.

"Oh, it's only a few hundred feet. When you get to the end, move over to the next row and work your way back. Keep moving over a row each time. It'll surprise you how much you can actually get done if you only keep looking at what's right in front of you. Don't focus on the whole thing, just work one step at a time."

Tom chuckled as he walked out of the corn field with its quarter-mile long rows. Alan could tell that Tom loved giving him the first lesson.

Alan slowly began to move down the row, looking for weeds. Some were small and others had gotten fairly large. Since Tom had run the cultivator through the field, the soil was pretty soft in between rows and wasn't easy to walk on. He could see his shoes were going to be a problem.

It took Alan about an hour to get to the end of the first row. He stepped out onto the road, turned around, and saw the house in the distance where he started. It still looked like a mile, he thought.

The sun was beginning to heat up and there was only a small breeze. He could see why Tom wore the brimmed hat. He would be blistered by the end of the day. And he needed gloves. He looked at his hands and could already see blisters forming. It was going to be a painful day.

Alan moved over a row and waded back into the sea of green. By the time he reached the end, back where he had started, he was tired and thirsty. He walked over to a nearby tree and sat down in the shade, and then looked at his hands again. Yep, blisters were now bulging in several places and he would need to find some bandages. He was quite aware that his back hurt, his arms and shoulders hurt, and that was only after one trip down the field and back.

Tom drove up in the old red pickup. "Hop in, let's go to Farm Supply and get you taken care of."

Alan groaned as he got up and limped to the pickup. He climbed in with a moan, put his head back against the seat, and closed his eyes. He was tired, and it had only been a couple of hours. How was he going to make it through two weeks?

At Farm Supply you could get boots and jeans, feed for farm animals, and parts to fix most anything on the farm. Alan grabbed a couple of pairs of jeans. Sally, the store owner, helped him find a good pair of work boots, hat, and leather gloves.

"Another one?" Alan heard Sally whisper to Tom. He pretended not to hear.

"Yeah, it seems they come around every few years," Tom whispered back. "This one wasn't a searcher like some of the others, he was more burned out, but he's determined." Alan held back a smile. Tom continued, "This morning was a bit rough for him, but that's how you learn."

"Well, just don't kill him!" Sally snickered, and then she proceeded to help Alan with his purchase.

After they left the store, they climbed back into the pickup. Tom said, "It's important to have the right tools and equipment for the job you're doing."

"So why did you have me start without the right tools?" Alan asked as he held up his hands with the blisters.

"Too many times we believe we know everything we need to, or we think we have the skills and tools we need to do a job," Tom explained. "But when we finally get into it, we find out we didn't know enough about the job or what was necessary to be successful at it. At that point, a lot of people usually quit or struggle to finish. With the right tools to start with, you have a better chance of succeeding.

"That's how it is with mindset too. If you don't have, or acquire, the right tools of the mind, you won't last long."

"So what are these 'tools of the mind'?" Alan asked.

"It all starts with your attitude." Tom pointed to his head. "The attitude that you will learn, that you will grow from what you've learned, and that you will never give up learning. Having an open mind for new ideas and concepts, new ways of doing the job, and a willingness to try them. Just like tilling the soil—once you start you need to keep it tilled, or it gets hard and unproductive. Keeping it tilled allows it to accept what's being planted in order to grow and prosper. If you keep the attitude of a continual learner, someone who's always ready for new ideas, you'll be well on your way to succeeding."

"I guess that's where I blew it," Alan said, staring out the window at the passing countryside. "I wasn't willing to listen to the new employees and their ideas. I thought, surely they couldn't have any good ideas, because they didn't have the experience I had. What I didn't see was that the world was changing and I wasn't changing with it. So when their idea for the new project was chosen over mine, I couldn't understand why. I guess my mind hadn't been tilled enough to accept new ideas."

"Tilled enough?" Tom interrupted. "I'd say it was pretty crusted over and not much was getting through. You certainly weren't open and receptive to new ideas or ways of doing business. Every business is constantly changing. If you're not prepared for that change, then you'll just be a dry, crusty field at the mercy of the wind and rain. Those are all the outside influences in your life."

Alan shot back, "Yeah, well, what about experience and knowledge? Doesn't that count for something?"

Tom suddenly slowed the pickup and pulled off the road into a field, causing Alan to sit up and look to see if something was wrong. They had stopped at the edge of a field. Tom opened his door and got out.

"Hop out, I want to show you something," Tom said, a stern look on his face.

Alan slowly slid out, his body now stiff from the morning work and sitting in the pickup. He followed Tom. There were two different fields. The one on the left was bare, and the one on the right was a sea of yellow about waist high.

"You see these two fields?" Tom pointed. "This one on the right is a wheat field, and it's getting near harvest time. It was tilled last summer to get ready for planting in the fall. Now it's going to produce a wonderful harvest."

Alan brushed his hand across the top of the golden wheat. The contrast between the two fields was stark and striking.

"But this one," Tom gestured at the field on the left, "hasn't been tilled in several years. The owner has stopped farming and isn't letting anyone else farm it. Tell me what you see."

Alan already knew where this lesson was going. "Obviously it's not very productive, unless you want to consider all the big weeds as being productive."

"You're right," Tom agreed. "But the important point to understand is that the soil's the same in both fields. It doesn't stop or change from one field to the next. But the attention and input each one has gotten is completely different.

"The wheat field has been tilled, fertilized, and taken care of every year, so it continues to thrive and produce a huge harvest. The other hasn't had any attention paid to it."

Kicking the hard, dry dirt, Tom continued, "When left to itself, it becomes hardened by the wind and weather, and the only thing that will grow are the dang weeds.

"At one time both of these fields were productive. But one of them stopped being tilled and nurtured. This is the danger of the attitude 'I learned it once and I have more experience.' If you're not continually preparing your mind to accept new information and ideas, you'll just become an old dried-up field full of weeds."

As they walked back to the pickup, Alan asked, "So how do you keep the mindset open to new ideas? How do you keep it from getting stuck in thinking you know better than someone who's younger than you? Someone who hasn't had the experience you've had?"

"It's all about commitment." Tom was leaning on the edge of the pickup bed. "You first need to commit to continual learning. And that learning can come from anywhere, even the younger employees. Everyone has their own life experience and understands life and society differently based on how and where they grew up. Don't be so quick to dismiss their ideas. It's even helpful to take a step back and honestly look at their ideas from their viewpoint.

"Once you commit to being open to new ideas, you need to have an attitude that all information is important. It may not be useful at the time, but some day it could be. And if you also have the attitude that everyone has something to contribute, you will find new ideas and insights in people and places you may have never found on your own."

Alan nodded and thought about the younger staff on his team at work.

"Have you heard the phrase 'there's nothing new under the sun'?" Tom asked.

"Um, I'm not sure."

"It was said by the wisest person to ever live," Tom explained. "He spent a great part of his life looking at the world, and experiencing all that life had to offer. He concluded that everything we need to know already exists, but it shows up in different forms.

"Each of us have our own unique thoughts and way of putting ideas together. The most important aspect of working with others is learning from them. No, actually, it's being willing to learn from them."

"Okay, I'll admit I wasn't willing to listen to the ideas of the new guys," Alan said sheepishly. "I've always thought you had to have the experience first, learn from people who have been doing it longer, and earn the opportunity to get your shot at a project or new position."

"If you're talking about an actual skill, that's still an acceptable practice—to learn from a master," Tom replied. "But you work in a field of ideas, and there's nothing new under the sun. Only new ways of putting information together. Who's to say someone with a fresh view or different outlook doesn't have a new way of putting information together in a manner not seen by others? Ideas are everywhere, and you shouldn't lock yourself into one way of thinking or looking at them.

"It's all in the mindset that you have to be open to new ideas. If your attitude is that you know best, then I'd say you'll be of no use in a very short time, because the world and business moves on."

"Well, I did kind of question why my boss would take the idea of someone who has very little experience in the job. I guess I'd fallen into a rut in my thinking and wasn't open to new ideas, no matter where they came from," Alan said thoughtfully.

"Okay then," Tom said with a cheer. "Let's get back to working on our soil. You still have some work to do, and so do I. The day won't stand still for us and the work will pile up if we don't get to it."

They drove back to the farm. Alan went into the house to bandage his blisters and put on his work boots. He really dreaded going back into the field in the heat of the day, but he did make a commitment to Tom. He set a goal to make it through to the end of the day, which he accomplished.

After a shower and dinner, it was all Alan could do just to stay awake. He was exhausted and had never worked so hard physically in his life before.

"What did you learn today?" Tom asked as they settled in the living room.

"I learned I don't like a hoe," Alan said somewhat jokingly. "I found I have muscles I didn't know about and tomorrow I'm sure I'll pay for it."

"Yep, it's not easy learning new tasks. This is the first challenge you will face. First, you made a commitment and willingly took off to accomplish the goal. Then you realized it wasn't as easy as you thought and began to struggle and slow down. Now, after facing the pain, you're wondering why you ever committed to it, asking yourself if there's a way out. This is the first real test of your stamina and commitment. Most people quit the first time it gets hard," Tom said. "But here's the important thing to know: in order to have any success in life you have to get the right mindset about it. Then you need to decide what it is you really want and believe without any doubt that you can have it or achieve it. You need to be able to see it in your mind, visualize the result that you want as if you already had it, and be willing to go through or endure whatever struggles, challenges, or pain you need to experience in order to get it."

Alan nodded his agreement. He had considered quitting. This was the hardest work he'd ever done. But there was also something satisfying about it—getting through the day, seeing the progress he made and the small successes as he reached the end of each row.

"I've never had to struggle with my work before," Alan responded. "It all seemed to come easily for me. I see now that when I came up against a new challenge and realized it wasn't going to be so easy anymore, that it was going to require more time and effort to compete, my response was to run away from it. I didn't quit, but now I see that running away from it even for a short time was an act of quitting."

"Sometimes we quit before we actually leave," Tom agreed. "I'm glad you hung in there today and kept at it. Success isn't measured in the end result, it's measured in the little progress you make every day, and the course changes or corrections you make when faced with an obstacle.

"You spent the day walking in a vibrant, growing corn field. That doesn't happen without the soil being fertile and filled with the nutrients it needs to support the growth that it produces.

"Remember, your mind is like the soil. Keep it fertile, keep putting good ideas in it, and never stop learning. And, oh yeah, you can learn from anyone and anything."

"Yeah, I learned I'm not too excited for tomorrow," Alan said with a laugh. "I've still got more to do out there. So I'm going to bed."

Alan limped off to his room, but before lying down he re-read Element One again three times.

7

Alan woke up to the smell of coffee and bacon again; it must be Tom's regular morning breakfast.

Stiff and sore from yesterday's work, Alan wasn't looking forward to another day in the corn field. But strangely, he was determined to keep his commitment to old Tom, and he wanted to get the rest of the Elements. He was beginning to see there was a lot he didn't understand about success. He had just let his future happen, he didn't really have a plan— and that seemed to work for a while but now it had caught up with him. He needed a plan.

"Good morning," Tom said, as Alan walked into the kitchen and poured himself a cup of coffee. "How are you feeling this morning?"

"Very stiff and sore. I haven't slept that well in I don't know how long."

"It's good for you to take on a new task. It allows you to stretch and grow your skills and knowledge. But to be successful, you need to make sure it fits with your overall plan. It must be part of the actions necessary to reach your goal. If you just go out and begin your day without a plan or a goal, you won't accomplish anything. If you don't plan your day, your day will certainly have a plan for you."

"Yeah, I get that," Alan replied. "And today my plan is to just get through the day."

Tom laughed loudly before heading out the door.

After a quick breakfast, Alan grabbed his gloves and hat, and headed back to the field where his trusty hoe was waiting. He'd already figured it was best to get an early start while it was cooler in the morning.

As he moved through the field, he began to take notice of the soil and how it supported the growth of the corn and the weeds; it even was home to small bugs. There were so many different kinds of weeds too. Some growing tall and upright and some that grew along the ground. Some were thorny and some had pods, like claws, that reached out and grabbed his jeans if he didn't spot them first.

Everything grew in the soil, and it was becoming clear you had to pay attention to what you let grow. Initially, it wasn't very visible, and if you didn't deal with it early on it would just continue to grow bigger and eventually take over. Not only that, if you didn't work to keep the soil fertile, as he saw in the two fields yesterday, only the weeds will grow and not the crop you really want.

Alan realized our minds were no different. If we were not careful about keeping an open mind to learning and new ideas, the stinkin' thinkin' of life would creep in and take over. A closed, crusted-over mind would not produce a successful outcome.

∽

That evening, after a long hot shower to ease the pain in his muscles, Alan sat quietly in the living room with Tom who was reading a book. It was the first time he'd noticed there were a lot of books laying around. He had seen the bookcase in Tom's office crammed with more books.

"Tom, I'm curious about something," Alan said, breaking the silence, "The rows of corn in the field are really straight—all of them. How'd you do that?"

"Ah, one of the great secrets about farming and success," Tom said as he closed his book and set it on the stand next to his chair. "Everything you need to know about succeeding in life you'll find out there in those rows of corn.

"Now, if you went out there without a plan and a goal of what you want to accomplish, you would just go wherever the mood or tractor takes you. You'd be less productive and end up with a big mess.

"The straight rows are more effective and productive. By knowing the size and dimension of the field, you can plan for how many rows you will need, how much spacing the seeds will need, and in total, how much seed you will need."

Alan nodded as if understanding, but he didn't see how it related to straight rows.

"But that's a discussion for later," Tom said leaning forward in his chair. "You asked me about the straight rows. Tell me, when you're driving down the road, how is it that you can keep the car going straight? Or when you're walking down a sidewalk, how do you keep from wandering back and forth across the sidewalk?"

"Well, I guess I look down the road or the sidewalk to where I'm going and make sure I'm always headed toward it," Alan replied.

"Yes, that is the goal to get to the destination. But HOW are you able to get there?" Tom asked, spreading his arms wide.

Alan had never really thought about how he got there, and he was pretty sure Tom wasn't asking about how a car worked or that you put one foot in front of the other when you walk. He paused and thought about it.

"I guess you stay pointed in the direction you want to go, and you have to keep adjusting your steering in a car depending on the road surface or the wind blowing, or if there are holes or bumps," Alan said, thinking about what you actually do when driving. "And I guess it's the same thing when you're walking."

"Okay," Tom replied, clapping his hands. "But where's your focus? Do you look only at the destination? Do you look only at what's in front of you?"

"I guess you do both." Alan was curious to know where this was going.

"Ah, you do both!" Tom said with excitement. "Here, let me give you an example." Tom got up from his chair and walked across the room. "Come stand over here. I want you to walk to the other end, in a straight line, and only look down at your toes, putting one foot in front of the other. Cup your hands around your eyes so you can only see your toes and nothing else. Do not look up, to the right, or to the left. Your goal is to reach that table by the window."

Alan did as he was told—he aligned himself with the little table and then looked down at his toes. He put his hands around his eyes and started walking, slowly putting one foot in front of the other. The carpet was a single color and gave him no clues to guide him.

After twelve steps, Tom told him to stop and not move. "Look up and see where you're headed."

Alan was shocked to see he wasn't lined up with his target anymore. Instead, he was pointed more toward the chair by the table.

"Huh," Alan said, now curious about this exercise. "I sure thought I was walking straight to the table!"

"Go back and try again," Tom suggested. "But this time, look only at the table, and I want you to hold your hands flat under your eyes so you can't see your feet. Again, one foot in front of the other."

Alan did as Tom directed, slowly walking toward the table. It was much harder to keep his balance not being able to see his feet.

After taking seven steps, Tom stuck his foot out in front of Alan and caused him to stumble. Tom grabbed his arm to steady him.

"What'd you do that for?" Alan shouted, catching his balance.

"Ah, there are many obstacles you either cannot see or are not ready for that come up not only in planting a corn field, but also in life. So you need to have a plan. Let's start with the first exercise," Tom said, sounding like a teacher. "If you only focus on your feet, or what's right in front of you, it may be possible to get to your destination, but you'll probably end up in the wrong place and then need to change course. Your path, or row in the case of the field, won't be straight at all. It's like driving a car. If you only focus on the road right in front of you, when it makes a curve or you come to a corner, chances are you'll struggle making the curve or miss the corner.

"In the second exercise, if you only look at the end of the field or the horizon while driving, you'll get there, but the changes in terrain may cause you to waver from a straight line—but you'll end up where you're headed. Any obstacle that jumps in your way you may not see until it's too late."

"Okay, I understand all of that. But how do you keep the rows straight?" Alan asked again, pointing in the direction of the corn.

"Not only do you need your end goal, your destination, but to get there in the shortest, quickest, straightest way, you'll need to have markers between here and there," Tom explained. "If you keep your markers lined up with your final goal, once you reach the first one, then you can focus on the next one. Keep doing that until you reach the final goal at the end. This allows you to make small adjustments as bumps and challenges pop up. You deal with one specific goal marker at a time, make small course corrections if you need to, but you should always focus on the end goal. A straight line isn't really straight; it's a continuous series of minor course corrections." Tom gave Alan a slight shove.

Alan was a bit confused. *Straight lines aren't really straight* he thought curiously.

"Whether it's planting a corn field or having success in life, you first need to have an eventual goal that you're focused on. It may be achieving a particular position in your company, running a successful business, or developing a new program or project. It could be having a family and being able to send your kids to college, or taking a dream vacation or buying your dream home.

"Whatever it is, you must start with the end goal firmly set in your mind. You need to see it, visualize it in your mind if it's not something that exists yet. Before I start to plant the corn, I see the straight rows of corn growing and how wonderful the harvest is going to be. You need to see what your goal is," Tom explained.

This was a bit confusing for Alan.

"And that means you need to have a goal," Tom continued. "So many people go through their life never giving a thought to where they want to end up. They just let life happen to them, and then they wonder at the end of their life why they never achieved much of anything. Or when the hardships in life come up, they say it's not fair or that nothing good ever happens to them, and they become angry or bitter. Some even run away from it or just quit."

Ouch, Alan thought to himself. He had run away when faced with the challenge of someone younger than him getting an opportunity he thought should be his. Yeah, he thought it wasn't fair!

"Yeah, I've been there," Alan said quietly. "Or maybe I am there. At least my goal was to reach the VP position. I thought if I kept my head down and did what was expected, it would be given to me. But I actually never made a plan to obtain it nor did I plan for the challenges I might face. I was just letting life, and my work life, happen. No in-between goals."

There was a moment of silence as Alan let his words sink in. Tom had paused, too, before responding, as if giving him time to reflect on his own words.

"It's the in-between goals, as you call them, that are the most important," Tom said. "Not only do you need to know where you're eventually headed, and have it firmly planted in your mind, but you need to plan the short-term steps to get there. Without those you'll quickly become frustrated or lost. You need to have some quick victories to keep you motivated to press on to your eventual goal. And when you reach the next short-term goal, it once again builds your confidence and gives you encouragement to keep going."

Tom walked over to his chair and sat down. He continued, "It's like climbing the stairs in a multi-story building. Why do you think there are only a few steps before there's a landing, even in between each floor? You can only climb so far before you need to rest. Then you can focus on the next landing which isn't so far away. If it was a continuous climb, you might think it's too hard or impossible, and you'd just give up.

"It's the landing, the in-between goal, which makes us keep climbing. Each time we reach one, we feel some satisfaction, gathering the energy to make the next goal.

"Even the GPS system that runs the map in your phone gives you in-between goals. You put in your starting point and your destination, and it gives you options on which route to take. Once you choose the route, it gives you all the course changes you need to make in order to reach your destination. If you miss one, it gives you a correction to get back on the path you've chosen. It's never a straight line."

Alan sat quietly, thinking about his life and his goal to become the VP in his firm. He'd always thought achieving it would happen in natural progression, by putting in the time, doing his job, and keeping their clients happy. Now that he had competition from some younger employees, he could see how having a plan he actually worked toward could be a benefit. And since his original plan wasn't working, he needed a new one.

"Okay, I can understand how the in-between goals are helpful," Alan said. "But how do you go about setting them so that you will reach your big goal? It doesn't seem to be very helpful to always be correcting your course, at least in big moves. And how do you pick the ones that will get you there the quickest?"

Tom sighed slowly shaking his head and rubbed his eyes. "Quickest? Why does everyone want to find the shortest route or the easiest way to success? I guess it's a sign of the times these days. We used to call it the 'microwave society,' because we learned we didn't need to wait for the water to boil or the food to cook in the oven. It's also been called the 'fast food society.' If we're not rewarded within a few minutes, then we go looking somewhere else.

"Now, I believe it should be called the 'connected society.' With these new phones everyone has, all the information you need seems to be at your fingertips. Even contact between each other is instant. We used to write letters, put them in the mail, and wait several days for them to be delivered and several more for a return answer. Now it's instant communication. No wonder you want the quickest way to your goal. It's what society today has come to expect and demand."

Tom was on a roll, and Alan could see this was a topic that got him really worked up.

"I agree that society has put a big emphasis on instant results," Alan responded. "But with our instant communication today, everything has speeded up. And if you don't participate you'll be left in the dust. So how do you set an eventual goal and the in-between goals, so you can reach them despite everything changing and moving so quickly?" Alan's tone was a bit skeptical.

Tom took a deep breath as if to calm himself. "When you drive a car at ten miles an hour down the road, you have more time to react to obstacles or bumps. It'll be easier to see them coming, which means you'll have time to go around or change course. If you drive down the road at seventy miles an hour, the obstacles and bumps are coming a lot quicker. So, what do you need to do to avoid hitting them?" Tom sounded tired.

"Well, you'd certainly want to look farther down the road, so you have as much time as you need to not hit them," Alan answered.

"Exactly!" Tom exclaimed hopefully. "You have to look farther down the road, and you have to be quicker with your corrections.

"In today's quicker society, once you set your eventual goal you need to determine the in-between goals that'll help you get there. Remember, the in-between goals are only guides or steps in the process. They are not the process. You'll need to be quicker in your thinking and changing of plans and the in-between goals as the challenges and obstacles appear."

"Well then, how do I set an eventual goal and the in-between goals to get me there?" Alan asked.

Tom leaned forward in his chair. "First, you need to decide what you want or where you're going. In other words, your ultimate goal is that one thing you want to achieve or have. You must be very specific and detailed about this. Once you identify this goal, see it in your mind as if you've already achieved it or gotten it. Use your imagination to feel the emotions you'd have from reaching this goal. Picture in your mind the people who'll be there with you to enjoy it. See clearly the opportunities you'll have and the things you'll be able to enjoy because you reached your goal. It must be so vividly pictured in your mind, with a firm desire to have it. Once you're able to see this, your mind will take over and begin to make plans and see opportunities you may have never seen or thought of before. It's your secret weapon in achieving your goals.

"Then you'll need to spend time identifying the action steps it will take to reach this ultimate goal. It may take years, depending on the goal, so you need to set the in-between goals that are the markers or action steps you need to get there. These will help keep you on track as milestones on your journey. They need to be as specific as the ultimate goal and firmly pictured in your mind. This planning takes more time and thought. You need to determine what it'll take to reach your ultimate goal. What education and resources will you need? Who are the people you need to associate and work with to help get you there? You need to identify all of the steps it will take."

Alan watched Tom get more energized as he explained this process.

"It's like planning a vacation," Tom continued. "First you decide where you want to go. You might find pictures of what the place looks like, imagine what it'll be like to be there and experience the scenery and culture. Then you decide how you're going to get there, the route you'll take, how long it'll be, what resources you'll need, the activities you'll participate in. Before you go, you even start picturing in your mind the feelings of enjoyment and relaxation you'll experience. In your mind, you see yourself already there.

"All of this must be written down. Write your ultimate goal on paper, describe it in detail with all the color and texture you can. Write down what you'll feel like when you reach this goal. It doesn't matter that you don't have it yet or you don't really know what it feels like, because if you picture it in detail with the emotion you want to have, and firmly believe you have achieved it, your mind won't know any different. It will immediately go to work on what's needed to have it."

This was starting to seem really strange, Alan thought. Why would your mind believe you had or were something that wasn't?

"How can your mind believe you have something that doesn't exist?" Alan asked skeptically.

Tom took a deep breath, sat back in his chair, and began again slowly.

"Have you ever known anyone who says 'I never win anything.' or 'I'll never be successful,' or maybe even 'I'll never have a nice house' or something similar?" Tom asked, looking tired now.

"Yeah, I have some friends back home who say they'll never be successful or have a lot of money."

"So what's their situation today? If they constantly make those statements to others—and it makes it more powerful when said verbally—then they're speaking a truth and desire into their minds. I'm going to guess they're not successful and maybe they feel stuck in their job. They certainly struggle with not having enough money."

"Yeah, looking at it like that, you're right," Alan said. He had never thought of it that way before.

"What they're actually doing is creating their own ultimate goal in their own minds," Tom continued. "They firmly believe what they're saying, and the emotions they put with their words, which makes it all the more certain their mind will do all it can to keep them from being successful. And any time they have a little bit of money, something breaks or someone gets sick. Something always happens to take the money away."

"Wow! That's absolutely what happens to them!" Alan said with amazement. "I've never thought about their words and beliefs causing it, I've always just thought they were speaking truth about the way it was. So, you're telling me that because they truly believed what they were saying, their mind created that reality for them?"

"Yes, exactly!" Tom said excitedly. "And if the mind can create a reality of NOT having success or money in your life, just think what might be possible if you firmly believe and can see in your mind, with all kinds of detail and emotion, the success you DO want!"

Tom let the thought simmer in Alan's mind. He knew the power of it. He, too, had struggled with his own success until he himself came across this concept. Once he fully embraced it and began to implement it, he saw his life change. As he focused more and more on the goals he wanted, it became clearer what he needed to accomplish in order to achieve them. That was how he started his own business and had the tremendous success that came from it.

Tom could see the look of shock and disbelief on Alan's face.

"That's it?" Alan exclaimed loudly. "All you have to do is dream it up in your mind in detail and write it down? If it's that easy, why aren't more people successful and have everything they dream of having? It can't be that simple."

"You're right," Tom agreed. "It is that simple, and it isn't."

Alan stared at him blankly even more confused by that statement.

"It is that simple," Tom explained. "The key for it to work is the belief. If you don't have a sincere, burning, committed belief in what you want or desire, it's just a wish. And then there's the work. You can dream, plan, and believe all you want, but if you don't take action—you, not anyone else—it still won't happen. That's why it isn't so simple. Most people aren't willing to put in the work necessary to reach their goals and dreams. To achieve any success, it takes hard work and commitment to make it happen."

Tom slid forward in his chair and looked intently at Alan. He said, "Once you create your ultimate goal and the road map to get there, all kinds of obstacles will start to appear. They'll come out of nowhere. And when you think you're well on your way and cruising along, you'll get run off the road. When that happens, you focus on your goal, figure out what went wrong, learn the lessons it can teach you, and start again from there." Tom gave Alan a little wink. "I don't want you to think it'll be easy," Tom continued. "You'll run into roadblocks, you'll have to face different fears—failure, change, uncertainty—and those are real. But if you want your ultimate goal, you need to ask yourself, 'Am I going to let that stop me? What is it I need to do to be more confident, or have more belief, in spite of the fears and challenges?' You got run off the road this week and tore up your car. Is that it? Are you done? Or are you going to pick up from here, set a new course to your goal or even change your goal?"

Tom let Alan think about that for a bit, and then he got up and walked over to his study. He came out with the same leather binder he had a couple nights ago when he gave Alan the First Element.

Tom went back to his chair and sat down with the leather binder in his lap. He gently rubbed his hand over the top of the binder, feeling its worn, aged surface. He hesitated to open it, looking up at Alan directly into his eyes, studying him for a full minute. Tom's vision blurred with tears. This binder, and all it contained inside, had once been his lifesaver, a real treasure.

"Alan," he began quietly. "Are you willing to commit the rest of your life to following this process? What I'm about to give you is the most important and most powerful of all the Elements. Everyone has it in them to succeed, but most won't do the work it takes. You can't give lip service to it. You can't try it and then put it on the shelf. You must follow this Element every day from now on. Will you?"

8

Alan sat quietly, looking at his hands in his lap. He realized Tom was about to give him something of great value. Was he willing to do whatever it would take? Could he make that commitment? Had he ever committed to anything in his life with that much seriousness? It was time for him to decide. He had a sense it will be the hardest thing he's ever done, but at the same time, he was beginning to see that it could have tremendous value and results in his life.

"Yes," Alan answered softly but firmly, looking Tom directly in the eyes.

Tom slowly opened the binder and removed another sealed envelope. Then he handed it to Alan. On the front was written, 'The Success Grower – Element Two.'

The Success Grower - Element Two
Focus on the Harvest

With your mind well prepared, set firmly the objective of your desire in your mind. See it vividly as if you already possessed it. Write it on paper in such detail as if it already exists as you desired. Describe it in all its color and sound. With as much detail as you can create in your mind's eye, tell how you will feel having obtained the objective of your desire.

When you have fully detailed the objective of your desire, begin immediately to put into practice these steps:

First, you must believe with all your being that you will have this goal. The words 'hope' and 'wish' are no longer a part of your vocabulary.

Second, place in your mind a picture of you having already attained it, what it feels like, and the joy you experience from having this goal or this life.

Lastly, read the full description of the objective of your desire out loud every morning upon waking and every night before going to sleep, with the picture of having attained it foremost in your mind.

This twice-daily practice will put your subconscious mind to work on finding the right path for you to take. It will identify the details and subsequent intermediate goals needed to continue on the path to the objective of your desire. Trust it, see it, believe it, do it, and you will achieve it.

Once fully described with as much detail as possible, contemplate on the necessary action steps and intermediate goals that will need to be taken to reach your objective. Begin with the end firmly pictured in your mind, working backwards by years, months, weeks, days until you have a determined plan—a road map—to reach the objective of your desire. Ideally, you will have action steps in your plan for the next 3 months, 6 months, and 12 months, and keep it constantly updated.

Do not be waylaid or discouraged by obstacles or challenges - they only exist for your learning and to test your determination and perseverance. Many who do not have an ultimate goal in their lives will try and dissuade you, but persistence along the path you have determined will lead to your success. Only you can travel the path and no one else.

*Grab **your FREE copy** (retail value of $147) of all eight Elements including a template designed to guide your growth to success, visit: **TheSuccessGrower.com/Elements** (no credit card required).*

∽

Alan tossed and turned in bed all night long, unable to sleep. As daylight began to lighten the sky, the birds singing their morning songs, Alan decided he couldn't lay there any longer.

Before he'd gone to bed, he had read both Elements One and Two. As he turned off the lamp on the nightstand, he had started picturing a future that had once been a goal when he began his career in marketing. One he hadn't thought of in a very long time. His goal was to establish his own marketing firm and work with some of the largest national companies.

Back then, it was only a dream, maybe a fantasy, but now it suddenly seemed more real. The pictures came flooding back into his mind. He was sure he even dreamed about it last night and wondered if that was what made him so restless.

Could this really work? Alan sat up and turned the light on. He rubbed the sleep from his eyes and read Elements One and Two again.

Alan had always heard about people who had written down their goals, carried the list with them or kept them where they could see them every day, and read them daily. He had thought it might be a good exercise. But he still thought you needed to find a career, work hard, and put in the time to be successful. And it seemed that was the way it worked for a lot of people.

Now he wondered if that really was their goal or if maybe they were stuck in a system that was rapidly changing, rewarding only a few. If that was all they wanted for themselves, then great. But whose goal were they really working on? Maybe it was the goal of the person who started or owned the business. If that was a goal or dream they had and became successful at it, who's to say someone else can't have a dream and work to make it successful?

Alan got up and stumbled his way to the kitchen. He found Tom at the table, drinking his coffee and reading the newspaper. The morning sky was only beginning to show a tinge of pink out the window behind him.

"How'd you sleep last night?" Tom asked, laying the paper down and sliding his reading glasses up on top of his head.

Alan poured himself a cup of coffee and, without looking at Tom, replied, "It was pretty rough. I haven't had such a restless night in I don't know how long." He walked over to the table, slid a chair out and plopped down on it.

"Yes, the mind is an amazing thing," Tom said quietly, seeming to be talking to himself. "When you give it a new problem to work on, sometimes it gets overexcited with all the possibilities. Tell me what you were thinking about when you went to bed."

Alan took a sip of the steaming coffee and pictured again the dream he had many years ago that had come flooding back in his mind last night. He stared into the black coffee and spoke.

"When I started my job at the marketing firm I was pretty young, and I had a lot of ideas about being successful in marketing. I used to think about what it'd be like to own my own business and represent some of the biggest national companies. The cities I'd travel to, the places I'd get to visit, and the food I'd get to eat. I could see myself getting awards and recognition from these companies and the marketing industry, for my achievements in marketing success and helping those companies grow their business and market share. I knew I was going to be the best, and everyone would want me to represent them."

The more he described what his dreams had been, the more he could feel the excitement he once had for his work and having his own successful business.

"But I guess it was only a dream," Alan finished quietly, his eyes drifting to the window and the brightening sky.

"So why did it come back again last night?" Tom asked directly.

Alan kept staring out the window. He was wondering the same thing, but he was also ashamed of the answer, of the possibility, that had been swirling in his mind since he got up.

"Nothing has been achieved in the history of man that wasn't first a dream," Tom said. "You had already created the ultimate goal for yourself several years ago. Like most people, you didn't know how to make it a reality, so you treated it more like a wish. We don't teach people how to be successful, we teach them how to be like everyone else.

"A few people figure it out on their own, who then teach or help others to reach their dreams. Since most people have given up on their dreams or never thought they could have them, they feel bad when others think they can succeed. Their natural tendency is to feel discouraged until the dream dies.

"I've seen it too often in my life. I was fortunate to have someone in my life who encouraged me to hold on to my dream and work hard on the path that would lead to its fulfillment. That's why I'm here today after having a very successful business career. And that's why you're here. Not because you had a wreck in the middle of nowhere, but because you were on a journey you weren't even aware of yet. To be successful in life and business, you need someone to help you, lead you, and guide you just like I had. You're not the first."

Tom's last statement caused Alan to snap out of the daydream. Shocked, Alan asked, "What do you mean I'm not the first?"

"There have been others who have come to our little town on their own journey. Most weren't aware of it, like you, but they always come. I'm here to teach, guide, and help grow the dream inside you that's been long forgotten or put away, because you think it's only a dream. I just help you find it again."

"So what happened to the others?" Alan asked, now curious.

"Some couldn't see the possibility anymore and didn't want to commit to the hard work it would take. Some developed the dream, set their ultimate goal, and were filled with excitement and energy. But the struggles and challenges of their life eventually beat them back down. And there are others who worked really hard, focused on their goal, and continued to grow toward their success. But right when they were about to make it, they ran into their own demons who destroyed it all," Tom explained.

"There are a very few who made it. They stayed committed to the goal they set. Their focus never wavered, despite the hard times, the roadblocks, the naysayers, the red tape, the dream-stealing friends and family—whatever it is that would try to beat them down. No matter what, they stayed focused on their ultimate goal and their success was even more than they could have imagined."

Alan sat quietly, wondering if he had the focus to make it into the second group.

"Those individuals are rare, I'm sad to say," Tom said more quietly. "Everyone has it in them to be successful. You just need to keep the dream alive, nurture it, till the soil, and stay focused on the goal and the steps to get there.

"That's why your dream came back last night. You created it a long time ago and have forgotten. But your subconscious mind never did. Last night it found a reason to bring it back up. Your mind is more fertile than you imagine. It's now time to start growing that dream."

Alan sat there in silence, looking at Tom in a new light. Before he had only seen him as an old farmer who once had a successful business. Now, it was like looking at a teacher. More than a teacher, though—there was a sense of calm wisdom of someone who truly cared.

"All right," Alan said, meeting Tom's gaze. "I'm in. Let's get started."

They walked out into a cool, breezy morning with the sun just fully above the horizon. Tom told Alan how he always liked this time of the morning when the sunlight lit up the trees and they appeared to glow. He stopped short of the drive and pointed to the shed in the corner of the yard.

"The lawnmower is in there, along with everything else you need to take care of the yard," Tom said.

"Wait, what about getting started on my goal and dream?" Alan asked somewhat confused.

"Oh, you'll be working on it too," Tom said with a sly smile. "I find the mind works better on a problem when you're not directly forcing it to. The conscious distraction of physical work gives your body something to do while the subconscious mind can freely grind away on the problem you give it. You've already given it the problem—I'm sure you haven't stopped thinking about it since you woke up. Now, focus your actions on mowing the yard and you'll be amazed at what your mind will do."

Once again, Alan was caught in his commitment. He trudged off to the shed with his shoulders slumped. He always hated mowing the yard growing up. That's why he lived in an apartment.

Tom briskly headed off to the shop with a big smile and a chuckle, as if he was amused at Alan's disappointed expression.

Alan slowly opened the shed and was dismayed to find only a push mower. The yard surrounding the house was quite large, with several big trees that not only provided nice shade in the heat of the day but also obstacles to work around with the mower. He realized this was going to take some time.

It was late morning by the time he finished with the yard. He was exhausted and his back ached from pushing, turning, and pulling on the mower. It was the weed eater that nearly did him in. He collapsed on a chair in the porch, dirty and tired.

Tom was right, he realized, as he sat there admiring the freshly cut lawn. Although he'd been focused on the task of mowing, his mind was filled with thoughts and ideas about the old dream he had of owning a marketing firm. He got excited about the possibility and could see in vivid detail the office he would have, the staff who would be energized with new opportunities, meeting with top-tier clients, traveling the country and vacationing in some of the most spectacular resorts, playing golf and relaxing on a beach.

He also realized he had not been using his time wisely the last few years. He had settled for the expectation of being promoted to a VP position in his current job, thinking it would be the next step up the ladder. What he failed to see was that he had stopped growing his own knowledge and skills to keep up with the changes in the industry and marketplace. Specifically, with the sudden growth of social media marketing.

Not only had he become comfortable in his job, he was just expecting the promotion because it was due him as next in line. He'd forgotten what got him there, his curiosity, hard work, creativity, and investment in the outcome for the client. All the same characteristics he saw in the younger staff that were now running the project he thought should have been his.

He knew how to do his job. His department was one of the more productive and successful in the firm. He had just not recognized the talent and skills of the new staff, keeping them from utilizing those skills to their best use.

Now he seemed to be at a crossroad. He could continue to work the way he had been, which would eventually result in no advancement in the firm, or worse. Or, he could embrace the changing market and learn from the insights and talents of the new, younger staff. He could be a guide for them and help them develop their skills to work with clients. This would give him the opportunity to better learn how to manage staff and develop a successful team for his eventual move into his own firm. If he was going to make his dream a reality, he was certainly going to need a plan.

Tom walked up to the porch where Alan was sitting. "Let's run into town and grab some lunch at the Sunrise Café. We can stop by the repair shop and check on your car."

Alan went inside and cleaned up a bit, changed his dirty, sweaty shirt, and then hopped into the pickup for the ride to town.

"You were right," Alan said after a couple minutes of silence. "While I was mowing the grass, all I could think about was the dream I've had about owning my own firm. I could see new clients seeking me out, excited staff, and being rewarded not just for the success of marketing campaigns but the growth it gave their companies. It's exciting to be a part of the growth and success of someone else.

"But I also realized I hadn't been working toward that dream anymore. Instead, I'd become satisfied with where I was. I thought I was in a system that would just reward me for the time I put in and the work I'd done. Now I see that I wasn't all that happy, and it was because I'd lost sight of the dream I had when I started."

Tom drove with a grin growing on his face, obviously pleased at this.

"And," Alan went on, "as the marketing industry changed, and the staff I have changed, I didn't see the opportunities to be a part of the change. Instead, I was trying to fight against it. That's not working anymore.

"But I still have my dream, and I still get excited when I think about it. I'm not ready at this point to make that kind of jump or career move, but I certainly see it's possible. I need a plan, and there's no better time than now to start on it."

Alan turned to Tom, who was now grinning from ear to ear. He asked, "So, what do I need to do?"

The café was just as crowded for lunch as it had been the other morning. Evelyn was there, taking orders and dishing out smiles and a good ribbing to the regulars. As they headed to the counter to take a seat, there was the same "Morning, Tom" greeting he'd witnessed before.

"Morning, Tom," Evelyn said as she placed a glass of sweet iced tea in front of him. "I see you have yourself another protégé?"

"Evelyn, I'd like you to meet Alan Morris. He's staying at my place for a little while, and I'm helping him learn about growing things," Tom answered.

"It's nice to see you again, Evelyn," said Alan. "I still have fond memories of that cinnamon roll!"

"Well, like they say, it'll never be better than the first time. And now you're going to have our famous chicken fried steak. Tom's probably got you working so hard out there you'll need a big lunch to survive!"

"Okay, thanks!" Alan replied happily. "I've learned a lot this week and worked harder than I've ever had, I guess. I'm a bit sore but it'll be all right."

Evelyn gave Alan a wink and said, "Well, Tom certainly knows what he's talking about. You're lucky you get to spend some time with him. He's pretty good at growing things."

"Oh Evelyn," Tom interrupted. "You always say the nicest things! Just bring us lunch, we've got a lot to do today."

After lunch, they drove to the Farm Supply for some parts and supplies, and then stopped to see Buddy at the repair shop. Buddy told them that all the parts he needed were to be here in a couple more days. He'd have it all fixed by the end of next week. They headed back to the farm. Alan sat quietly, staring out his window, watching the countryside go by.

"Alan," Tom said, breaking the silence, "do you like what you do at your marketing job?"

Alan had been thinking about that very question, wondering if his dream was what he really wanted or was it something that had excited him when he first started his career. He thought about all the companies he had done work for, some more successful than others, and how he'd been part of some really great marketing campaigns, helping companies grow their businesses.

"Yeah, I do," Alan said softly, still watching the fields go by his window. "I really do. I get to work with really great people, and the thrill of learning about a business and the new product or service they want to market is very invigorating. I spend a lot of time getting to know them, why they are in business, and what their business goals are. I like to find out how they serve their customers. Then we're able to focus on the message we want to put in the marketing materials. Some work better than others, but when we hit a home run, it's a thrill for everyone!

"I like that. It's not so much about me and the firm, but it's more about their success. If they succeed with their marketing, then the firm succeeds."

Alan turned and looked at Tom. He added, "But it seems to be changing these days. I see so much attention put on the success of the firm and bringing in new clients and a big focus on the bottom line. It's putting a strain on everyone, and I feel the reason they have turned to some of the younger staff is because they feel they might have new ideas and their knowledge of social media will help improve the business.

"But the business is still a people business. If you don't spend time getting to know your client and their business, and how their product or service will help or benefit their customer, it doesn't matter what media you use for your marketing it won't be successful."

Alan slumped down in the seat. Tom didn't say anything, waiting for him to let it all out.

"I do like my job," Alan said again. "But I think we've lost sight of our own purpose at the firm. Or maybe it's me that has lost sight of the purpose. I need to figure that out."

When they got back to the farm, Tom took Alan inside and had him sit at the table. Tom went into his study and returned with a notebook and pen, and set them in front of Alan.

"I want you to spend the rest of the day writing," Tom instructed. "You've read Element Two. You need to put your dream on paper. Writing it down makes a connection, and transforms the wish or dream into something more tangible. Once you have written it down, it becomes more real to you, something that your mind will work on to achieve.

"I want you to write several different sections. The first is to fully describe the life you'd like to have three to five years from now. Ask yourself, what is it you desire to accomplish, to have, to do, to be. Make sure it includes all areas of your life: personal, physical, and professional. Things like family, relationships, health, spiritual, financial, accomplishments, recreation, possessions, community, service to others, vacations, whatever you desire your ultimate life to be. Don't just focus on your professional life, you are more than your job. Describe your life as you want it to be.

"Take them one at a time. See in your mind what your ultimate goal looks like in five years for each one, as if you already had it that way. It's difficult for most of us to imagine our future beyond five years. The key is to see it and describe it as you want it to be."

Alan sat and stared at the notebook in front of him.

Tom continued, "Since your dream is centered on your job, begin there. See it in your mind and write down what you are doing. Where are you working, and what does your office look like? Who are you working with? Do you have a business with a lot of staff, or are you working alone? Who are your clients and what kind of business are they in? What is your annual revenue? How much are you paid? Keep asking questions until you describe it fully.

"Then move on and describe these specifically: your home, your car, your finances and investments, your family life and relationships, your physical health and exercise, your personal life and personal development, and the community you live in. Describe each one with as much detail as you can. Include what it looks like and what you want to have as a part of that dream. Keep asking yourself 'what else' until you uncover in your mind all the desires you have for each one.

"This should take some time. Be thoughtful and deliberate. Ask your mind to show you what each area of your life would look like. If you need to take a break, do it; if you want to sit outside, go outside. This is a time to release your mind and let your desire flow onto the paper.

"When you finish, we'll begin the next step. We're told that *as a man thinketh in his heart so is he.*[4] Our minds are more powerful than we ever imagined. You can create your future—it only takes vision and belief."

Alan was trying to digest all of the instructions. Tom went back to work plowing the field next to the corn field, leaving Alan to work on his assignment.

Alan took a deep breath and sighed. "This is going to be a lot of work," he said out loud.

He took the pen and wrote 'JOB' at the top of the page and started writing.

That evening, Alan was exhausted mentally. It was easier to write down his vision of his work life a few years from now as he would like it to be, but it was harder to think about and see what he wanted his personal life and relationships to be. He'd always been so focused on his work.

Eventually, the writing became easier, and his thoughts were filled with details of a life he wanted for himself. He remembered he used to think about some of these but just passed it off as only a wish. Now, as he continued to write and dream about the future life he wanted, it seemed to be more of a possibility. He was actually able to see it more clearly in his mind now that he had described it in detail.

Tom eventually came back, having spent the afternoon on the tractor. He was dusty and tired, and went to clean up. Alan rummaged through the kitchen and put together dinner.

"How'd it go today?" Tom asked as he sat down at the table to rest.

"It was one of the hardest things I think I've ever done. I've never taken the time to think about the future or what

I want my life to be in the future, especially in that much detail," Alan said as he set plates on the table.

"Most people don't." Tom nodded. "We don't teach anyone that they can design the life they want. Oh, a lot of people have dreams and wishes, but they learn really quickly to keep them to themselves because they're teased about it or slapped down by those who have given up on their own dreams.

"The key to achieving what you have written down today is first just that, you wrote it down. Now it has some reality to it. The next key is belief. You must fully and completely believe you can have it as you described it. If you held back in any area because it seemed your dream was too big to imagine, you have already started to limit your belief. What you desire in your mind, in your heart, is something you can have. You must believe it, pursue it, and not waver from it." Tom stirred sugar into his iced tea. And then he continued, "The wisest man to ever live said to his son:

'Above all else, guard your heart; for everything you do flows from it. Let your eyes look straight ahead; fix your gaze directly before you. Give careful thought to the paths of your feet and be steadfast in all your ways.'[5]"

Alan was curious about who this wise person was. He put dinner on the table and sat down.

Tom watched Alan intently. "We don't teach that much anymore, especially to our children. Your mind and belief are the most powerful tools you have. Don't waste them."

"I've never really been taught that," Alan agreed. "I was always told to go to college, get a job, and work hard. Nothing about setting goals for where I want to go in life or that I can have the things I dreamed of as a kid, or even as an adult. Most people just laugh and call you a dreamer.

I guess it's because they've given up on their dreams, and it would make them feel bad if you went after your own."

"It doesn't have to be that way," Tom said. "You've already started down the road to your goals and the dream you have identified. Even if you stop there, you'll be more successful than most people because you wrote it down. Your subconscious mind is already working on how to make it a reality.

"The next step, and this is what you'll work on tomorrow, is to work backward to identify the steps you'll need to take today, to start making progress toward your goal. Take those five-year goals you have written down for each area of your life, and then set milestones to reach along the way between today and then. This will give you the in-between markers to aim for. Then you can begin to identify the steps, activities, people, and resources you will need to get there.

"If you can plan out the path to reach those goals in five years, you'll be surprised at the doors that'll open for you along the way."

Now Alan really wondered what he'd gotten himself into. This sounded like a lot of hard work.

"When you were out in the corn field hoeing weeds, did you notice anything about the corn?" Tom asked.

"Well, we've already talked about the straight rows," Alan said, glancing out the window. "I guess something else would be that they're evenly spaced apart?"

"Yes, the rows are evenly spaced apart. What else?"

"Well, let me think about it. Umm, each corn plant seemed to be evenly spaced in the row too?"

"Excellent!" Tom shouted and slapped his hands on the table, startling Alan. "They are evenly spaced for several reasons. One is so they can most effectively pollinate the ears of corn when they emerge. It also allows for the most efficient use of the space, moisture, and nutrients. The ultimate purpose is to have the most production possible from the space and conditions the corn is growing in."

Alan poured himself another glass of tea and refilled Tom's. He picked up their plates and put them in the sink to be washed, then returned to the table.

"That's what your next step is all about," Tom said quietly. "This is the most critical step. And now you need to work on breaking down your goals into smaller, manageable steps.

"This is called 'planting.' You've already planted the seed for your success by putting your goals into your mind and on paper. Now you need to space out the steps along the path to those goals, into easier-to-achieve steps. If you try to go too far too fast, you'll only stumble and get discouraged."

Alan noticed that Tom already had the leather binder laid on the table next to his chair. He was excited and nervous to get another Element. It just meant more work. Tom picked up the binder, carefully caressing the aging leather again, and pulled out another sealed envelope. He handed it to Alan. On it was written, 'The Success Grower - Element Three.'

Tom yawned and stretched, said he was tired and headed off to bed. He stopped at the doorway and turned to look at Alan. "Don't forget to read your five-year goals out loud before you go to bed. You'll feel foolish at first, but you'll get over it. When you wake up in the morning, your mind will have worked on it all night. It might surprise you what ideas you'll come up with to reach your goals."

Alan nodded.

"Sleep well," Tom said as he closed the door.

The Success Grower – Element Three
Plant Seeds for a Bountiful Harvest

Ideas are like seeds. They have no worth until they are firmly planted in fertile soil. It's only after they have been planted and covered over that they begin to warm and germinate and come to life.

Your thoughts, habits, and ideas need time to germinate and grow. Do not rush the process of growth. Make certain to take time to contemplate your goals, your future, and the path you will be taking.

The milestones along the way to your goal should be progressive. They must begin as simple steps to allow for a progressive, paced, and orderly process, which will help you learn to do the harder work later.

Plant seeds for a bountiful harvest. Few seeds yield many more but do not accumulate to sustain an ever-increasing growth.

A seed has within it the ability to produce many times more than the seed itself. But it does not remain as the seed, it must change.

"What you sow does not come to life until it dies."[6]

The seed must die in order to produce. So you must commit to give up yourself, take the focus off yourself, in order to reap a bigger harvest. You have within you the ability to produce a great harvest. Plant the seeds of your ideas. Develop the regular habit of planning. Take the opportunity to sit quietly and contemplate the future and growth of your ideas. Create within yourself the habit of regular discipline to work toward your goals. Small, steady steps yield a more consistent and larger harvest.

Walk in integrity. Who you are is what you choose to become. Become a person of integrity. The integrity of a seed yields a multiple of the same seed. Without integrity, you have corrupt seed.

Plant the seeds of success and integrity. Tend to them every day. A bountiful harvest is waiting for you.

---

*Grab **your FREE copy** (retail value of $147) of all eight Elements including a template designed to guide your growth to success, visit: **TheSuccessGrower.com/Elements** (no credit card required).*

9

Alan woke feeling refreshed and rested. He could remember dreaming last night about the life he had written about yesterday. It didn't seem to be so far out of reach as he'd thought. After reading the goals and dreams he'd written down the day before, Alan wandered into the kitchen.

It was a bit later in the morning than the last couple of days, and Tom was already out working. He had left the coffee on, so Alan poured a cup and sat down at the table with his pen and notebook to begin working on his plan.

It wasn't easy trying to figure out the actions and steps he needed to take to get to his goal in five years. Focusing on each different area of his life was both invigorating and depressing. He had never really thought specifically about making a plan for his relationships, physical health, or personal development.

It seemed normal to plan your career—to a point—but he had let that kind of just happen.

It took him all morning to work through about half of his long-term goals. He started with his career/profession since that was something he actually had thought about over the years. Now with a plan for where he wanted to end up in five years, he was able to begin to identify the steps and milestones he needed to hit along the way to get there. That one was pretty easy.

By working on each area separately, it was easier to identify some of the major milestones he would want to accomplish. Once he had those, he came up with smaller goals he could reach. Then he began to break those down into monthly and weekly actions.

Alan went to sit on the porch to think about the goals he was writing and what his life would be when he accomplished them. He noticed a car coming down the road; it slowed and turned down the drive to the house. He was curious who this might be. It then occurred to him there had been no other visitors to Tom's house since he'd been here.

The car went around the house and parked in the back. Alan got up and followed, wondering who it was.

The driver got out and saw Alan, and walked up to the house. He was a tall, middle-aged man with graying hair.

"Hi there," he said as he came up to Alan. "I'm Cal Winthrop."

"I'm Alan Morris."

They shook hands, and Cal asked, "Is Tom around?"

"Yeah, he's out on the tractor plowing the field over there by the corn. It's about lunch time so I expect him to be in shortly. Is there something I can help you with?"

"No, I was traveling near here and decided to take a detour and come see Tom. He's an old friend and mentor, and it's been a while since we've seen each other. How's he doing?"

Alan heard the tractor coming through the field toward the house.

"He's good, I guess. I've only been here for a few days, haven't known him very long. But you can ask him yourself, it looks like he's headed this way."

Tom pulled the tractor up next to the shop and slowly climbed out. He dusted himself off as he walked up to the house. When he saw who the visitor was, his entire face lit up into a big smile and he nearly began to run.

"Cal, my dear friend, it's so good to see you again! It's been a while since you were here. To what do we owe this pleasant surprise?"

Tom grabbed Cal's hand and shook it briskly, and then wrapped him in a big bear hug.

"Come on in and have a glass of tea and a sandwich. Tell me everything you've been up to since we last talked. I see you've already met Alan. He's a visitor here for a short time, and I think you'll both enjoy getting to know each other."

Over lunch, Cal told Tom all about his work and business and how it continues to grow every year. He showed pictures on his phone of his wife Sandy and the kids, and his new granddaughter, Nicole. Tom was intently focused on everything Cal told him and was genuinely excited about the growth and success of his career and his family.

Alan sat at the end of the table, listening and watching the interaction between Tom and Cal. He couldn't remember the last time someone was that genuinely interested in his own life. What a great relationship they seemed to have.

"Alan's on a journey just like you were, Cal, when you came here the first time," Tom said, now looking at Alan. "He's just learned that his future is up to him to design and create the way he wants it to look and not leave it to chance. He's been working on his goals this morning, it looks like."

"Did you start him out with the hoe?" Cal asked with a laugh.

"Yeah, it's a great way to see if they can make a commitment and keep it," Tom said, laughing so hard he had tears in his eyes.

Alan knew they were poking fun at him. Then Cal became serious and looked directly at him.

"It was ten years ago when I first came to Tom's place. I was 48 and working in a bank as the vice president of Loans. It was a very successful bank, and I had worked with most of the business owners in town on their commercial loans. I enjoyed my job and the people I worked with, but I felt like something was missing in my life. I had a nagging feeling, that little voice in your head that said there was something else I was supposed to be doing.

"I didn't have a clue what it was or what it should be. I kept working but couldn't shake it. It got to the point that I'd just show up at work and do my job without a lot of enthusiasm or enjoyment. I faked it pretty good, but I wasn't happy. It started to affect how I treated my family, and I spent most of my evenings and weekends watching TV."

Alan could certainly relate to that. He didn't have the enthusiasm he used to for his job, either.

"One of my customers was expanding his business, and we were working on the details of a new loan package," Cal added. "Part of the collateral he put up for the loan were some buildings and farm land out this way, and in my due diligence, I needed to come look at it and take some pictures.

"It was in the middle of the winter with a huge storm forecast for the area. A blizzard was coming, so I wanted to get in quickly, look at the property, and get out. I stopped at the Sunrise Café for a cup of coffee before leaving town, with the wind and snow already howling. Then I learned the highway out of town had been closed. That's when I met Tom."

"I get it now," Alan interrupted. "The Sunrise is the key to success!" They all had a good laugh. Cal continued, "He invited me out here, and I spent the next three days waiting for the storm to blow through and the highway to open up. We talked a lot about being intentional in your life and having a plan for your future. Tom gave me the first two Elements before I left, and I made a commitment to come back in the spring for a week and get the rest of them.

"With only the first two, I was able to see a new exciting future for my family and a new path for my career. I hated to leave knowing there were more Elements. It made for a long winter until I was able to come back."

Cal turned and looked at Tom with sincerity and appreciation, who was beaming like a proud father.

"Now, I am a financial consultant and counselor with the bank. I realized what had been nagging me was that many of the business owners I worked with really didn't have anyone looking out for their overall interests. I now work with high net-worth individuals and businesses to help them develop a plan for safeguarding and growing their assets. After I developed my plan, it became obvious we needed to be doing this at the bank since we already handled their financial business. It would be easier, and better, to create a division in the bank to do consulting and creating plans to ensure these individual assets were protected.

"The business grew quickly because they were already customers of the bank and had a relationship of trust. Now I'm the vice president of the division, and I'm being groomed to replace the president who will retire in eighteen months. I never would've imagined I'd be doing this if I hadn't met Tom, who helped me see I could create the future I wanted instead of just letting the future happen to me."

"Yeah, we've had that discussion," Alan said, nodding at Tom. "I've gotten the first three Elements and I'm working on my goals and plan now. So how many Elements are there?"

"There are eight in all," Tom injected. "You'll be getting one each day now."

"You're working through the hard part now," Cal said, turning to Alan. "But don't think the rest of them are any less important. They will keep you grounded and moving forward, even when you face hard times."

"So you believe this is the reason for your success?" Alan pointedly asked Cal.

"Most definitely!" Cal shot back. "Oh, I suppose you can do this on your own, but you really need someone to guide you through it. Someone to call you out when you're getting off track or falling back into old habits.

"That's why I come back to see Tom whenever I get a chance. His advice and counsel are what have kept me on track and grounded. I don't get by here as much anymore, but it's always refreshing when I do. He's been my mentor for ten years now, and you'll be glad to have him as yours."

The conversation turned to Cal's family. He and Tom spent the next couple of hours talking about Cal's work, the success he was having, and some of the challenges he faced. Tom spent most of the time listening, asking probing questions and helping Cal develop a plan for continued growth in his relationships and career.

Alan had never been a part of such a productive conversation. He was looking forward to his progress and Tom's approval.

Cal looked at his watch and said he needed to get on the road. He warmly shook Tom's hand and turned to shake Alan's hand.

"The time you have here with Tom is special. Learn all you can and be determined to work toward your goals. Your future success is up to you, but you need someone to guide you. Tom's been a friend and mentor, and I will always seek his advice. There will come a day when he won't be here anymore, so it will be important that we continue to help each other."

Cal told Alan to call him anytime if he wanted to talk. He got into his car and drove off, waving as he headed out to the road.

Later that evening, sitting in the living room, the conversation turned to the progress Alan was making on his plans and goals. Alan talked through each of the areas of his life he had listed. He described his life as he wanted it to be in five years. He also talked about what his ultimate goal, or vision for his life, looked like many more years in the future.

Tom told Alan that he was pleased to see that Alan had not only created a path to his goals in three years, but was also thinking about and writing what he wanted for his life in the long term.

They spent the evening discussing each goal. Tom asked questions about the steps Alan needed to take to accomplish them. When some of the steps weren't clear, Tom would probe deeper with more questions, making Alan look at his plan from different angles, identifying obstacles that might come up and how he could deal with them.

"You've done good work today, Alan," Tom told him as he sat back in his chair. "This is the first place where most people get frustrated and stop. It's hard to think what actions you need to take to reach your goals and dreams. Most people just have dreams, and that's all they have. You'll hear them say, 'Someday I'll have…' or 'I wish I could…' or 'If only…' Those are the words of people without a goal or a plan. They end up letting life happen to them instead of taking charge of their life and circumstances."

"It's easy to play that game," Alan added, knowing exactly what it was like. "That's pretty much been me. I guess that's why so many people stay in jobs they don't necessarily like, because they don't have a plan to change it and grow.

"I can already see so many possibilities for my future just having gone through this work today. I'm more excited about my future now than I have been in a long time." Alan closed his notebook.

"Wonderful!" Tom said, clapping his hands together. "Now you're ready to learn the hard part!"

"Hard part?" Alan shot back with a look of surprise. "This was pretty intense thinking about how I was just showing up in life. It was hard to identify exactly what I want my life to be and look like. And not being at that point already, how do I really know the steps I need to take to make it happen? I thought this was pretty hard!" Alan felt a bit defeated.

"You're right," Tom replied, "it is difficult to get your life and plans on paper. We're not taught how to think about the future and how to design our lives. It's a new thought process, and creating something that previously didn't exist isn't easy.

"But now that it does exist, in your mind and on paper, it's the challenges and obstacles you will face along the way that can put you in the ditch again."

"Thanks for bringing that up again!" Alan frowned.

"No, truly, now that you have created your goals, the next few weeks and months will be the most difficult. At times, everything and everyone will seem to be working against you and the goals you set. Don't take that as a reason it won't work or that you shouldn't be pursuing your goals. That's when you will know that you're on the right path. Most people don't like to see others succeed, it makes them feel bad because they don't know how to achieve their own goals and dreams. So they will do and say whatever they can to discourage you."

Alan scowled. He wasn't happy to hear this.

"I've seen it over and over," Tom continued. "At that point, you only have two choices: one, listen to them and fall back into what's easy and comfortable and a life of unhappiness; or two, take it as a sign you're on the right path, and up ahead is the accomplishment of your next goal. It's your choice. It's the hardest right before a victory."

"But what if it truly doesn't, or isn't going to, work out?" Alan asked exasperated. "What am I supposed to do then?"

"If you have sincerely worked at it with the firm belief it's what you want, but you keep encountering roadblocks, that may be a signal you're on the wrong path and you need to adjust. At that point you probably need someone else to help you determine if a change needs to be made or you're still on the right track.

"That's one reason why Cal comes by on occasion, or calls me," Tom explained. "Some of the others do the same."

"How many others?" Alan asked with surprise.

"You are number twelve."

"Do you hear from all of them?"

"Not all," Tom said quietly, his eyes beginning to fill with tears. "Each one of them has so much potential. Some were struggling with jobs and careers, others were looking for a way to change their relationships with their family. Everyone is different, but the solution is basically the same. It comes down to actually having a plan for those things in your life you want to succeed at. No one teaches that in school."

"How do you make sure you keep working toward your goals? I know that when I get back into the routine of my job and life, it'd be very easy to slip back into the comfort of the job and let others make the decisions for where my life goes. How do I keep that from happening?" Alan asked.

"Like I said, now the hard part begins. It's part of life. Will you stay focused on your goals and dreams, or will you give in to the illusion of an easy life? When your future hangs on the day-to-day decision of another person, I wouldn't say that's an easy life. Most people say they like the 'security' of a paycheck. How secure is it really, when on any given day someone else can determine your future? Even if you like your job, you still need a plan to succeed in that job and for the potential changes that might come too."

Alan crossed his arms and slumped down in the couch. He thought about the work it was going to take to stay on the path to his goals. It wasn't going to be easy.

"So what's the solution to stay focused and not fall back into my old routine?" Alan asked curiously.

"First, keep doing what you are doing now. Read your goals and dreams out loud every morning and evening. That will keep you centered on where you are headed. When you don't stay focused on where you're going, you'll start to drift.

"Second, read. Read books, articles, magazines—anything that encourages you to grow in knowledge about your job, your goals, and your own personal development. Be a continual learner and reader. There's so much negative thought and conversation in the world today, you must combat it with positive and encouraging thoughts. You do that by reading good books. Read every day, even if it's only for a few minutes, but do it every day.

"Third, get a mentor. That's why Cal continues to come back. I suppose it's easy to choose me since I helped you start down this road. I'm glad you were able to meet Cal. He's also a good mentor to have. Just be sure to choose someone who has either done what it is you're wanting to do or has at least walked a similar path to achieving their own goals.

"We all need someone to talk to, to bounce ideas with, and to keep us on track. When you're in the middle of your journey, sometimes you'll run into walls or obstacles. Your mentor should be able to help you refocus or identify the cause of your struggles, and help you keep moving forward. If they try to give you the answer, they're not being a mentor. A good mentor helps you find the answer and will call you out when you're focused in the wrong place.

"And fourth, say 'Yes' to new experiences and opportunities. Not so you get bogged down with a lot of responsibilities and commitments, but so you can continue to grow your knowledge and skills. Just be cautious to not fill your time with activities and responsibilities that don't lead to the achievement of your goals. You might be surprised where you can learn and who you can learn from. Maybe those 'younger staff,' as you call them, have something you need to learn from. None of us have all the knowledge, and each of us have our own special skills and talents. Everyone can teach you something. Never stop learning, never stop growing." Tom sounded like a teacher again.

He continued, "Your life is not a hobby. You must have a purpose for your growth and learning. We work on our hobbies when we have time. To have a successful life, you need to commit to continual learning and personal growth. So much of the time, I see people working 'in' their lives instead of working 'on' their lives. Be committed to working 'on' your life, because at the end of the day, you're the only one who can be in control of your life and your future."

Tom handed another envelope to Alan. "It now comes down to being patient with your commitment. Growth takes time and effort. It needs to be tended to every day. You have to give it the proper tools and nourishment to grow.

"You'll get a new envelope every evening now for the next few days. Follow the same process, stay the course, learn all you can while you're here, and always believe in yourself."

Alan took the envelope. The words 'The Success Grower - Element Four' were printed on the front.

The Success Grower - Element Four
Water and Fertilize for Healthy Growth

Nothing survives without water. Not only does it keep us alive, it helps flush out toxins and impurities that invade our bodies. But water alone doesn't maintain healthy growth. A continual supply of nutrients is needed for strong growth, to enable us to withstand the challenges of life.

You must put good resources into your life. Knowledge is the source of all sustained growth. It is a finite and stagnating resource unless it is continually refilled. Once you stop learning, you no longer will be able to see with clarity the path you are on, and the influences of the world around you will begin to creep in and overtake you.

Read. Stretch your thinking. The writings of others will bring you new ideas and concepts, which will help you see new opportunities and paths to reach your goals. Daily reading is a must in order to grow. It is the fertilizer for your growth.

The more you read and learn, the deeper your understanding and growth will be. Develop an intense desire for obtaining knowledge.

Don't walk the path you have chosen alone. It may be a path that only you are on. Find a mentor, someone who has walked a similar path, who can guide you and keep you headed toward your goal. Be careful in choosing your guide. Confidentiality, honesty, and forthrightness are a must.

Be strategic with new opportunities. Consider them carefully in relation to the achievement of your goals. Activity for the sake of wanting to be helpful to others is not always the proper action to take. Do what needs to be done, help those who need your help, and stay focused on your own growth.

Put these into practice, and your knowledge and skills will continue to grow deeper and stronger. Consistent watering and beneficial fertilizing will yield strong roots and quicker, sustained growth.

*Grab **your FREE copy** (retail value of $147) of all eight Elements including a template designed to guide your growth to success, visit: **TheSuccessGrower.com/Elements** (no credit card required).*

10

It was well after sun-up when Alan awoke and stumbled into the kitchen, following the aroma of fresh brewed coffee. He was surprised to see Tom sitting at the table. Most mornings he was already out in the shop or on the tractor. And he wasn't wearing his usual bib overalls.

"Good morning!" Tom said cheerily. "How'd you sleep last night?"

"Morning," Alan mumbled, still rubbing the sleep from his eyes. "Good, I guess. I was worn out after all the mental work yesterday. What's up today? Taking the day off and not going out to work?"

"Nope, today is a day of rest. Remember last night I talked about increasing your knowledge and resources, the nutrients, and how you need them to sustain and even increase your personal growth? And that you need a mentor or someone to guide you?"

"Yeah, I thought about that when I went to bed," Alan said as he pulled out a chair and sat down. "Reading I understand, because I can read books and magazines or articles on the Internet. But the mentor is harder to figure out. You're here, and that's great, I can talk to you in person. But what happens when I get back home and into the daily grind? I guess the phone will have to do." He shrugged.

"Yes for us it will have to do. But you need to make sure you have good resources nearby. Let me suggest a book to have in your library and some mentors." Tom picked up a book from the table and handed it to Alan. It was the Holy Bible. "I read a bit of this every day."

Tom added, "Like I said to you the first day, there's nothing new under the sun. Everything you want to know about achieving success you can find in there. You'll even find some great mentors, or role models, for every stage of your life.

"Today is Sunday I always take this day as a day of rest. I also go worship with other believers. You're welcome to come with me if you want. It's your choice."

The offer, oddly, didn't surprise Alan.

"As a kid, I used to go a lot with my parents. I haven't done that in quite a while," Alan said as he thumbed the pages of the book. "I haven't read this in a long time either. I thought some of those things you said were familiar. But I don't really have anything appropriate to wear, so they'll have to take me like I am."

Later that morning, Tom and Alan took a drive across the county to look at the different crops growing in the fields and to get a better appreciation for the work that went into each one. Alan was curious how some of the farmers were more meticulous about their fields than others who seemed to be behind on their work or didn't care so much how it looked.

Some of the fields had beautiful crops of corn with their long and wide leaves, and there were other fields with weeds growing up taller than the corn. It was obviously going to be a problem at harvest time.

They came to a field that was a golden color, and the wind seemed to roll across it like waves on the sea.

"What's that?" Alan blurted out in amazement.

"It's a wheat field, and it's almost time to harvest. Isn't it beautiful?" Tom said with pride as he slowed down to get a better look.

They drove around for what seemed like hours to Alan. He had come to appreciate Tom's farm and the corn, and how much work it was to be a farmer. But just driving around looking at everyone else's fields was tiring. Tom would slow down to get a better look, and at times would stop and get out to walk into the field. Sometimes he would go into a corn field and see how the corn was growing, and then he would walk into a wheat field and pluck a couple of the wheat heads. He'd rub them between his hands to separate the seed from the head, and look at it to see if it was ready to harvest.

It was all a mystery to Alan, and somewhat boring, since this was not anything he knew about. He had never given much thought to where the food that he ate came from, but he knew a lot of it came from or contained either corn or wheat. Because of that it was interesting to him. Now, he would always have an appreciation for the food he ate. It sure took a lot of work just to get it to his table.

Eventually, they rolled back into town and stopped at the Sunrise for a late lunch. The café wasn't as full as Alan had seen it the other times he'd been there. Evelyn was still there starting to clean up and getting ready to close for the day.

"Well, good afternoon, gentlemen," Evelyn said as they walked through the door. "Have a seat, and I'll get a couple specials out to you real quick."

"What's the special?" Alan whispered to Tom as they slid into a booth along the far wall.

Tom looked at Alan with a sly grin, winked and shrugged his shoulders.

"Oh, it's always a mystery, but it'll be the best meal you've had in a while. Especially since you've been eating at my place all week!" Tom said with a laugh.

Evelyn brought over a glass of iced tea for each of them. Then she came back with two plates of the special. It smelled wonderful, Alan thought, and he suddenly realized he was pretty hungry after their long drive around the countryside.

"Roast beef, mashed potatoes and gravy, green beans, and a salad," Evelyn said with pride. "It's the last of it, so you made it here just in time. I've got some peach cobbler and ice cream for dessert, just let me know when you're ready for it."

Alan dug in to the meal. He couldn't remember a time he'd tasted roast beef so tender and delicious, and the mashed potatoes were creamy smooth. To top it all off, the hot peach cobbler with vanilla ice cream melting through it was just heaven in a bowl. *These farmers sure know how to cook*, Alan thought to himself.

Tom wiped his mouth after finishing his cobbler, leaned back in the booth, and spoke in a serious fatherly tone. "Alan, it's been good to have you here. You'll be leaving this week, and I truly hope your life has been changed. I see in you a person who can dedicate himself to his work and keep to his commitments. I've given you some of the timeless elements for success, whether you use them for your career, your personal life, your relationships, or whatever, the process will always work as long as you follow it and work it."

"And I truly appreciate it," Alan added sincerely. "But why did you choose me? How did you know I was worthy to be given the Elements?"

"Well, first of all, I don't really believe that I chose you. I believe you were chosen and sent to me. It was no coincidence that day you first came here, that the only empty seat I would find was next to you, don't you think?

"You see, although I've already lived a life of great success in business, I chose to create a new path of success. After my wife died, my drive and enthusiasm for my career became meaningless. I had lost the most important person in my life, but I had not really made her the most important. I had given that "honor" to my career. In fact, I had given so much time and energy to the success of my career that even my children wandered off on their own lives and we didn't have much of a relationship."

Tom paused a bit, choked back some emotions from the memory, and then continued.

"I decided then to change my own goals. I wanted to make sure I could help others find success in their lives as I had in mine. But I wanted to make sure I helped them focus on all the areas of their life."

"We haven't talked about that much since I've been here," Alan said.

"No, we haven't. That's because it's easier to get you excited about a successful business or career than your personal life. You've talked some about your parents, but you haven't said anything about being married or having a girlfriend."

"I was married once, a few years back," Alan responded. "She already had a baby when we started dating. It was always great to be together, and I really enjoyed the baby and watching him grow. We got married, but it only lasted a couple of years. I guess we had different ideas for our futures, and looking back on it now, it seems we were both inflexible. So we split up. I haven't seen her or her son in about three years."

"I'm sorry to hear that," Tom said quietly. "Just like no one teaches us how to set goals and plan for a successful life—which we typically define as a career—no one teaches us how to be successful in relationships either."

"Nope, I never got any of that," Alan assented.

"But I'll strongly caution you not to place that responsibility on your parents today," Tom said, pointing at Alan. "As an adult, you're completely responsible for yourself. I put some of the responsibility on society. That's why I think one of the most important books you can read for success in all areas of your life is the Bible. Don't neglect that one."

Alan thought about how his life and relationships have gone so far in his life, and he wasn't happy with the track record he had. Now, he seemed to have been given a second chance and he really didn't want to mess it up.

"You asked me how I knew you were worthy to get the Elements. Well, it doesn't always work out this way," Tom said with a grin. "But after I gave you the hoe on the first day, and you took off into the corn, I had hope!"

"A hoe? That's what you based your opinion on? A hoe?" Alan exclaimed in amazement and laughed out loud.

"Not so much the hoe itself, but the fact that you kept at it all day in the heat of the sun and wind. Then, you went back out there the next day to finish what needed to be done. I didn't ask you to finish it; you obviously saw the task that needed to be done and you figured out how to get it done. It was the commitment and determination to finish that told me you would follow through with the Elements.

"I showed you the weeds and how they get their roots into the soil. They start out small but eventually become so big you have a hard time getting them out. So let's talk about the weeds and how they can take over if we don't pay attention to them. I'm not just talking about the weeds in the corn, I'm also talking about the weeds that grow up in our lives. Let's head back to the farm and I'll show you." Tom slid out of the booth.

They said goodbye to Evelyn and climbed back into the pickup, and headed off to Tom's farm and another lesson for Alan.

They walked into the corn field where Alan had first learned to use the hoe. The corn seemed a bit taller, Alan thought curiously.

"Look out across the field," Tom said. "It looks pretty uniform and clean on the surface just looking at it. But take a little bit of time and really look at it." He pointed at something to their left. "Over there, oh about six or eight rows over and down the row a ways. See it? The weed that's poking its head up above the corn? And let's see, there's another one off to the right just a couple rows, and another one over by the road. Keep looking and you're sure to find more."

"But I thought I got all the weeds!" Alan exclaimed with disappointment.

"Ah, but weeds are sneaky little devils! The ones that grow out in the middle between the rows of corn are pretty easy to see and deal with. It's the ones that grow in the row of corn that are sometimes harder to see. They'll even grow up right at the base of a corn stalk, which makes it even harder to get to them without damaging the corn."

Alan slumped his shoulders because he was sure he had done a good job. It seems no matter how hard you work, it's either not enough or just maybe there will always be weeds to deal with.

"Look here." Tom knelt by the corn. "You came through here a few days ago. Now I didn't expect you to get all the weeds since this was your first time with a hoe in a corn field. You can see there are some small ones you missed. Others that were too small to be seen easily before are now pretty obvious. And look, there are even more tiny ones starting to grow."

"So what's the use hoeing them or using your cultivator thing on your tractor?" Alan asked, feeling nearly defeated.

"The weed seeds are always in the soil," Tom replied. "There are a lot of ways to deal with them. Before the corn seed is planted, the field is plowed and cultivated to not only make it easier to plant but to minimize the growing weeds. Then as the corn is growing, the cultivator on the tractor is used to knock down the majority of the weeds growing in between the rows. You can't get every one of them, so you're just trying to give the corn a chance to grow up big and strong, eventually shading out a lot of the other weeds."

"What happens with the ones you miss and that grow big like those?" Alan asked, pointing to the tall weeds he missed.

"If you cultivate the field properly, before you plant and while it's growing, there are some that'll still survive. Hopefully it won't be a lot. When its harvest time, the equipment is designed to handle and mostly eliminate the weeds from the crop seed," Tom said as he stood and stretched his back. "It's no different with our lives. Weeds are a part of life, and there are many different kinds. Some of them we plant ourselves, but many are just lying dormant, waiting for us to start watering and fertilizing. Then they spring to life."

"What are the weeds in our lives?" Alan was now intrigued by this lesson. "And how do we plant our own weeds?"

"Most of the weeds we plant are our own beliefs, habits, and self-talk. When you get back home, it won't be long before your old habits will rear their heads and tell you how comfortable they are. You'll be tempted to believe your life wasn't so bad, and you'll start asking yourself why you even want to go through this change. You'll begin to tell yourself it's too hard, you're not good enough, you don't really have the commitment to succeed, or that all this talk about goals and dreams is just a fantasy. You'll be tempted to give in and fall back into a life that feels comfortable. But you won't be happy if you do. There will be a nagging feeling from that point on in your life that you could have done something better. The 'what if' will haunt you," Tom said, walking out of the corn field with Alan close behind.

"Then there are the weeds that others plant," Tom continued. "At first it'll appear as if they're trying to help. Your friends will give you their advice or question why you would even think you could do something different and go for your goals and dreams. Although they will sincerely believe they're giving you advice so you won't be disappointed, they're actually working to keep you in their comfort zone.

"Once you believe you can achieve your goals and start making progress, they'll stand in your way, because your success will make them feel bad about themselves, that they gave up on their own goals and dreams a long time ago. They'll try to project their own fears and anxieties on you. You have to be strong enough to let them go."

Alan stopped and immediately pictured in his mind which of his friends would do that.

"And then there are the weeds that lie dormant until we plow a new path toward our goals," Tom added. "These are the challenges that come up along the journey that at times appear to be impossible to get around. It might be corporate policies, governmental rules, changing economies, the demands of customers, or a whole host of other problems. Some, yes, are roadblocks. You either find a way around them or decide to take a different path.

"That's why cultivation is so important. Like we talked about several days ago, our mind can be fertile soil as long as we take care of what goes into it and what we think about. You will never get rid of the weeds, you just need to learn to control them and not let them take over your mind and thinking. If you wait too long to deal with them, they will go to seed, and then you'll have even more weeds to deal with. At some point you get overrun with weeds." Tom gave Alan a slight shove. As they walked up onto the porch to sit in the shade, Tom said, "The only way is to never lose focus of your goals and where you're going. Even with the tractor and cultivator, if you don't watch where you're headed you can tear up the corn. Never lose sight of your goal. Follow the steps for a fertile mind, and water and fertilize your thinking and your plans for strong and solid growth. That's the only way you'll be able to overcome the weeds and reach a successful harvest."

Alan thought about some of the weeds in his life. He could see how easy it would be to fall back into the comfort of the life he'd been living. All of this thought of setting goals and working to fulfill a dream of success, even though it was exciting and created hope of a better life, it was also scary. He had already been thinking about what his friends would say. Would they be supportive or critical? He was beginning to understand what some of the weeds he was going to deal with when he got home. And they will be some big ones.

"How do I keep my mind and plans cultivated to minimize the weeds?" Alan asked, now looking a bit dejected. He was struggling with the idea of facing a change in his life, but Tom just smiled, as if he thought this was a good thing, a good sign.

"Follow the Elements you've already been given. Read and fill your mind with good ideas and uplifting information every day. Get around people who are supportive and ready to help you on your journey. Believe this is possible for you, read your dreams and goals every day, and eliminate as much of the negative thoughts as you can. This is your goal, it's not anyone else's, and it's yours to fight for."

That evening, Tom handed the next envelope to Alan labeled, 'The Success Grower - Element Five.'

The Success Grower - Element Five
Cultivate Your Mind and Plans

As with fertile soil, a fertile mind grows what is planted. Care must be taken to ensure that seeds which will produce a bountiful harvest are planted and not neglected. If neglected, they will wither and die.

Weeds are a part of life. But they do not need to control your life. To continually cultivate your mind in order to minimize the influence of the weeds is a practice that will lead to a healthy and vibrant life designed to reach your goals.

Cultivating your mind isn't just attacking the weeds that come up, it is the constant, ongoing process of adding good, positive ideas and thoughts. If you don't attend to it for a period of time, your mind will become crusted over with the hardships of daily life, and the crop you have planted for a harvest will begin to shrivel up. The weeds of despair and self-doubt will creep in, and if there continues to be no cultivating of the mind and plans for growth, they will eventually turn into more weeds.

Your focus must be on your goals. Do not lose sight of them or let the weeds grow. You'll never get rid of them. But with a process of regular cultivation of your mind you can control them.

True cultivation comes from learning. Never stop learning. The world constantly changes—new ideas, new businesses, new inventions. The one who fails to keep learning and growing new ideas and plans will fail to reach the success they desire.

Your mind is a fertile soil. Your goals and dreams are seeds worth growing. Be your own success grower.

11

A loud clap of thunder jolted Alan from a deep sleep. Another blinding flash of lightning, followed immediately with a deafening *bang* told him a storm had come up in the night. The wind was blowing with a force strong enough to knock you over if you stood outside. Rain beat against the window so hard Alan thought it might break. It was still dark outside. The rapid flash of lightning was like a strobe light freezing the trees in stop-motion fashion, bending wildly in the wind.

Then the hail started. At first it was just a few, but they hit the side of the house and the roof with such force it sounded like someone was throwing rocks against the wall. It grew heavier, and the roar of the wind and pounding of the hail sounded frightening.

Alan threw on his clothes and stumbled quickly to the kitchen where he found Tom standing at the window, watching the fury of the storm. He noticed Tom was soaking wet. Alan shouted over the roar of the storm, "What happened to you?"

Tom was startled and jumped, unaware of Alan's presence.

"The storm woke me up, and I remembered I had left the Mercedes sitting out so I ran out and put it in the garage. I just made it back in before the hail started," Tom said with a calm sadness.

"It sounds bad. What's this going to do to your corn?" Alan asked as hail continued to pound the roof of the house.

"Yeah, this is a bad one. It doesn't look good for the corn or the rest of the crops. We'll find out when the sun comes up." Tom had to shout over the roar. He kept watching the storm out the window, small pools of water puddling around his feet. He looked down and finally noticed. "I guess I better get out of these wet clothes."

"What are you going to do?" Alan shouted as Tom headed for his room. He was alarmed at the damage being done by the storm. "Aren't you worried?"

"Yes, I am worried." Tom stopped to look at Alan. "I'm worried for Albert down the road. He has cows out in the pasture who are taking a beating from this hail. And I'm worried for Frank and June, because they never take the necessary action to prepare for a storm like this. If it's hitting them like it is here, they'll be devastated. And there are a bunch of others like them. Yes, I am worried."

The storm only lasted about thirty minutes. The light show was the most spectacular of all. Alan was mesmerized watching the tops of the storm clouds illuminated from inside the cloud. He had never witnessed such fury and beauty at the same time.

It was still a couple of hours before daylight, but sleep was no longer a possibility. Alan walked outside, the air now cold from the passing storm and the ice that covered the ground. He had never seen hail like this. In the light from the porch, he saw most of the hail was the size of marbles. But there were many the size of golf balls. He was sure it had done a lot of damage to the corn.

Then he saw the big ones. He picked up a couple he guessed were as big as a baseball, and walked back into the house. He put them on the kitchen table and sat down, just staring at them and slowly turning them around, fascinated by how a storm could create such big balls of ice.

Devastated, Tom had said. That was the right word for it, Alan thought.

Tom came back into the kitchen and saw the hail stones on the table. He put some coffee on then pulled out a chair, sat down, and picked up the hail.

"This was a bad one, all right," Tom said looking the hail over. "A pretty bad one."

When it was light enough to see outside, Tom and Alan walked out to the corn field. It had rained enough during the storm that the field still had some standing water, so they weren't able to go in any farther. But they didn't need to—they could see the result of the storm well enough from where they stood.

What was once a quickly growing sea of green, that was nearly chest high, was now merely bare stalks, only knee-high tall and mostly stripped of their leaves. The hail had beaten the corn severely, leaving it lifeless, bent, and broken.

They stood there quietly surveying the devastation.

Alan glanced at Tom, expecting to see a look of defeat and grief. Instead, he appeared calm and just stood there with his hands in his pockets. Alan was feeling a sense of loss and despair because he understood now that this was the livelihood of a farmer. The cost of seed, fuel, and equipment just to get a crop growing, plus the time and effort spent fertilizing and cultivating—all was now lost with nothing to show for it.

"Stupid storm," Alan muttered kicking at the mud and broken corn stalks. "What are you going to do?"

"Storms come, Alan, and we can't change that," Tom said softly.

"Yeah, I know, but this is your life!" Alan exclaimed angrily, pointing at the beaten corn, tears now starting to swell in his eyes. "You worked hard to get to this point and now it's all gone! I know I've only been here a week, but I put some work into that corn too. I still have the blisters!" Tears rolled down his cheek.

"Alan," Tom said, putting his hand on Alan's shoulder. "It'll be okay. But right now we need to go check on Albert and see if he needs any help with his cows. There's nothing to do here."

They hopped into the pickup and made their way slowly out of the water-filled, muddy drive, heading down the road to Albert Clark's place. As they carefully drove down the muddy road, it was obvious the damage from the hail was pretty bad.

Alan couldn't imagine how you would be able to continue after a loss like this. All the time and money put into a crop to just have it destroyed in less than half an hour. This would be too much stress for him. He didn't think he could handle being a farmer.

Tom, on the other hand, didn't seem to be concerned about it. At least not outwardly. Maybe he was torn up on the inside, Alan thought, but he sure wasn't showing it. Alan was both concerned and curious by Tom's lack of reaction to the storm.

They found Albert just leaving his place to go check on his cows. As they met on the road, Tom rolled down his window and told him they would follow him to see if he needed any help.

The pasture wasn't too far away, up a very muddy, winding trail. It looked to Alan like the storm hadn't been quite as bad here. He didn't know what a hail storm would do to cows, but he figured it wasn't good.

Albert opened the gate and Tom drove through into the pasture. They found the cows all huddled together in the corner of the pasture. To Alan they seemed to be all right. Then Tom pointed to some cows in the distance, lying in the pasture. Albert headed off toward them and Tom followed.

Albert got out of his truck, walked over to the cows who were obviously dead, and just pushed back his cap and rubbed his forehead. This was definitely a big loss for Albert. He bent down and gently patted the dead cow then walked over to the other one and did the same.

"I'll need to get the tractor up here later and get them moved out. I need to go check the others over real good to see how injured they are," Albert said sadly.

"Albert," Tom said. "You know to call me if you need any help. You just call, all right?"

"Yeah, I'll call you. Thanks, Tom," Albert said, shaking Tom's hand. He turned to Alan next. "It's Alan, right? Well, thanks for coming and checking on us."

They shook hands. Tom put his hand on Albert's shoulder, looked him in the eyes, and reminded him to call. They got back into the pickup and headed out of the pasture and onto the road.

The morning sunlight brought out others to look at the damage done by the storm. Alan wasn't sure if it was curiosity or what, but Tom joined them, driving around and checking on the other fields.

"Well, it's not as widespread as I thought it might be," Tom said. "The wind and the rain would have done enough damage to the wheat that's ready for harvest and some of the corn will be blown over, but those will be okay."

A couple of miles from Tom's place there hadn't been any rain. All the crops looked okay. Tom pointed out some of the wheat fields that had already been harvested and how those farmers will be thankful they dodged this storm. They slowly drove by his wheat field again. Tom said it would be harvested this week. Eventually, they returned to Tom's place, which seemed to have suffered the most severe damage.

Alan noticed tree limbs littering the yard, broken off by the storm. Even most of the leaves on the trees around the house had been stripped off and now were a matted mess in the yard. The house also had taken a beating, and a new roof was going to be needed.

"I guess you'll be calling your insurance about the roof on your house," Alan said, looking at the damage. "But what about your crops? It looks like most of your corn is completely destroyed, but you don't seem to be too upset about it. It's not even mine, and yet, I'm feeling like I just lost something really important. Are you okay?" Alan was concerned about Tom's silence.

Tom parked the pickup next to the yard to avoid all the mud.

"Alan," Tom said, shutting off the engine. "There are some things in life we can control and many we can't. The weather is certainly one we can't. It all needs to be part of the plan. Storms of many kinds will come up in life, and if you are not prepared for them, you suffer from the damage. That happens too often with most people. Because they weren't prepared, or hadn't taken any precautions, they end up devastated. Storms will come, but they usually only last a short time. Then the sun will shine again.

"If you haven't taken the time to develop a good strong plan, the constant challenges of life will beat against you to break your resolve. Outside forces and pressures will always be pushing against you. It's like that corn field." Tom pointed. "If it's not well cared for and planted in fertile soil, and fertilized for strong growth, even the constant winds can break it over because it's weak and won't be able to withstand the pressure.

"Other times, you'll be faced with the overload of duties and responsibilities, and you won't be able to focus on your goals or give them the attention they need. It will feel like you're drowning and not getting anywhere. The risk is you will be tempted to just sit there, stuck. That's why starting with a fertile mind and a step-by-step plan will give you the focus to put those goals in order.

"Too much rain on unprepared ground will just sit there and not soak in, like it would on a cultivated field. And, if it sits too long it will start to smell. If we wallow in despair every time there is a storm in our life, we end up with *stinkin' thinkin'* and a bad attitude. At that point, it's pretty hard to find your way out.

"That's why you need to have a plan, even for the storms." Tom gestured at what was left of the corn.

"Okay, but how do you plan for something like this?" Alan asked.

"Well, just like you have insurance on your car and your house, you can also insure a crop. It depends on how much you want to gamble on the weather or the chance of a devastating loss like this," Tom explained.

"I'm sure that can be pretty expensive, and I'm guessing a farmer doesn't make a whole lot at the end of the day anyway?" Alan asked.

"That's true, but you have to consider the risks and decide how you'll handle them. Then you build those costs into your plan. Or, you may decide to head in a different direction. So, take this corn field as an example. I had some insurance on it, so that'll help recover the cost and some of the lost revenue. But, since it's still in the middle of summer, I can work to get this field plowed and ready to plant wheat this fall for a harvest next summer." Tom's words revealed why he had been so calm. He added, "Just because a storm blows through doesn't mean it's over. There are always options. You just need to make those options part of your plan.

"While you are working on your plans for your goals, take some time to figure out what the storms are that could come up and either bog you down, cause a delay in your plans, or completely destroy the plans you made. If you do that now, and also have a plan to deal with them, you won't need to have the stress and heartache and despair about everything being lost."

"But how do you know what to plan for? How can you know what those storms will be?" Alan asked, now looking concerned.

"You won't know specifically each one, but initially, you can plan for them in a broad sense. It might be financial or your health or your family or regulations or a lack of staff or customers. It could be dealing with people who constantly question what you're doing and trying to take away your dream. Start with the bigger picture, identify what the obstacles or roadblocks might be, and come up with two or three options to move past them. That way, when they do occur, you will already have considered and planned a way around them. Storms, obstacles, and roadblocks are all the same, and you just need to be ready for them," Tom said as he surveyed the damage around his house.

"Are there any you just can't recover from?" Alan asked.

"Yes, there are, but that is a matter of having a prepared mind or not. It's all up to the mindset you have about the storms. If you're determined to move past them as they occur, options will be obvious for you. But if you let them control you and your decisions, you'll stay mired in the mud of the storm. The destruction will be much more difficult to overcome. It all comes down to how you prepare your mind and the thoughts and information you continually put into your mind. It's also the people you associate with and the ones you choose to avoid."

"I don't know how you do it," Alan said, shaking his head. "I'd be a mess, but it sounds like you have already planned for disasters like this and know what your options are. I'm guessing a lot of that comes with time and experience too?"

"Yep, experience is a wonderful counselor," Tom agreed. "The sad thing is, most people don't actually learn from experience, they just let it determine the path they take. The great thing about experience is you can also learn from the experience of others. Watch how other successful people deal with their challenges and roadblocks. You don't always need to come up with the solution. Someone else has already gone through it or faced it and found a way to succeed. Take some time and look at how they handled it, then just maybe it will also be an answer for you."

"I guess I have a lot to work on. Now I need to think not only about the weeds and irritations that pop up but also the bigger storms that could derail my plans to reach my goals. I think this will be harder, but I can see it will make a big difference in my attitude and how I handle these storms. Because I'm still torn up about your corn!" Alan said with a bit of a chuckle.

"All right," Tom said, getting out of the pickup. "While I've got you worrying about me, let's get these tree limbs picked up in the yard before it gets too hot. The humidity today will be a killer."

That afternoon, Tom was on the phone with a neighbor asking him to harvest his wheat field. The storm had slowed them down, so they now had time to get to some of the smaller fields that weren't rained on.

"Tomorrow," Tom said to Alan with a happy tone. "George is going to cut the wheat tomorrow. I'm glad you're here to see it. That's what this is all about. When you finally reach your goal and reap the harvest, it's a huge relief and a sense of accomplishment. Enjoy it in the moment, and then move on to the next one."

"I'm looking forward to that." Alan sat by the kitchen table. "If you don't mind, I'd like to run into town and check on the car. I'm hoping Buddy will be finished with it in a day or two, and I'd like to get an idea about the cost. I'm sure it's not going to be pretty. One of those storms that popped up in my life, I guess, huh?"

Tom laughed. "Yeah, let's head to town. There's not much more we can do out here this afternoon until things start to dry up."

The drive gave them a better look at the extent of the storm and the damage caused by the hail. It was heaviest in a path a couple of miles wide that went right across Tom's place. Just a few miles away, it didn't look like there had been much rain.

Alan was glad to see the storm hadn't gotten into town. He was concerned about what the hail might have done to his car, but he saw that it was still sitting inside the shop.

Buddy was busy underneath a pickup and slid out when Tom and Alan walked in.

"Morning, guys," Buddy said. "I heard the storm was pretty bad out your way, Tom. How much damage did you get?"

"My corn's a complete loss," Tom replied. "Albert Clark lost several cows. It'll be a struggle for him this year."

"Wow, that's too bad," Buddy said, wiping grease off his hands. "I'm glad it stayed down that way and didn't come through town. I've already had several calls about replacing windshields. Looks like I'll be busy for the next week or so.

Alan, I got your transmission in this morning and you're up next. I'm guessing it'll be ready in about three days. If I don't get started on it this afternoon, I'll get to it first thing in the morning. That's my priority until it's done."

"What's this going to cost me?" Alan asked, feeling the knot in his stomach growing.

"Since it's a foreign car, it took a bit to find the right tranny, but I have connections in the city and was able to get you a little better price. It should run around four thousand, total, including the tow, parts, and labor. I know that's pretty expensive, but that's how it is with the parts for these cars," Buddy explained.

"Yeah, well I was expecting something like that. I'll be able to cover it, I'm just glad you're able to do the work."

"Don't you worry, it'll be good as new when I'm done. I've worked on these before. I'll take care of you, don't you worry," Buddy said with a wink at Tom.

"Okay thanks, Buddy, I really appreciate that." Alan shook hands with Buddy, and then he and Tom left.

"I guess I'm pretty lucky to have all this happen here," Alan said to Tom as they got back in the pickup.

"What do you mean?" Tom asked, grinning curiously.

"Well, due to my stupidity, I had an accident just outside a town where I would meet you in a crowded café with only one seat left next to me. The mechanic in this town just happens to have experience working on foreign cars and transmissions like mine. It seems odd he would settle for running a repair business in such a small town."

"Is it?" Tom asked. "A guy has a dream to own a repair shop where he can take care of people and make sure they not only get a good deal but good service. I'm sure he could do that in a bigger city, but he'd never make the personal connections and build relationships with his customers. Sometimes, bigger isn't always better."

"Yeah, okay, I get that but...wait..." Alan stopped. "Buddy is another one?"

"Yep, he wanted to run his own shop and was tired of the typical auto repair business that focused more on working quickly instead of taking the time to do it right. For a lot of people, their car or pickup is the most expensive thing they own. Buddy cares about your car because you care about it. He knows most people don't think too highly of auto mechanics, and that they never seem to fix the problem just so you have to bring it back and they can charge you again.

"Not Buddy. He will fix a lot of things he's not asked to fix, not because he wants to run up your bill but because it's the right thing to do. A lot of the time he doesn't charge for a simple fix. If it's bigger, he'll let you know so you can decide. Otherwise, it's his way of providing better service. He believes if he goes above and beyond what's expected, he'll develop strong loyalty and relationships with his customers, so that he'll never be lacking in work," Tom explained.

"Well, he certainly knows how to make you feel confident in his abilities," Alan added.

"And he'll be the first person to tell you if he can't fix it. He'll also help you find someone who can that he respects to do the job right."

"Why did he choose to have his business here?" Alan asked, looking around at the small town.

"While he was looking at the vision for his dream to have his own repair shop, he realized what excited him the most was serving people and giving them the best experience. He figured that in a larger city he would be spending more time and money on advertising, trying to find good help, and competing with bigger shops. Once he put his goals on paper, it became clear to him he needed to find a place where he was needed. When he started looking, he found it right here in front of him. His goal wasn't about having a big business and making a lot of money, it was about using his talents to serve people in need."

Alan sat quietly as they drove out of town, thinking about that and his own goals. What frustrated him was how so much of his time at the firm these days was taken up with the business side of his job; how this project will affect the bottom line, how much time and staff it will take, and could they work on multiple projects at the same time. It seemed he was being asked to focus more on the impact to the firm than actually developing a solution for their customer.

Somehow, that didn't feel right any more. Obviously, those issues needed to be considered to run a successful company, but it seems the priorities were somewhat skewed. He would need to think about that more when he reads back over his goals.

Back at Tom's place, Alan was brought back to the reality of the storm and its destruction that morning. It was beginning to dry out a bit and the humidity hung heavy in the air. It was obvious now to Alan that the corn was a huge loss. In the sun and heat, what was left of it wilted, turning gray.

"Wow, I'd forgotten about all of this for a little bit," Alan spoke up. "I was feeling pretty good about things until we got back here. It looks even worse now."

"Yeah," Tom said with a heavy sigh. "It takes a lot to pick up after a storm like that. But that's why you have a plan. You make a plan for the good times and you make a plan for the worst times. Then you're just working the plan, not wallowing in despair and indecision."

"That's a trait I'm going to have to work on," Alan admitted. "I guess my response to my latest storm was to run away and not deal with it. Since I didn't have a plan for it, I just blew up and left. Now, I've got a lot of work to do when I get back just so I can move forward again."

"Cleaning up the mess we leave behind is usually a hard thing to do, especially if it involves the feelings and actions of others," Tom said as they walked into the house.

Tom disappeared into his study and came out a few minutes later holding another envelope. He handed it to Alan, and written on it was 'The Success Grower - Element Six.'

"It's important you understand this one." Tom sat down in his chair. "It's about storms that appear in our lives. Most of the others didn't have the chance to witness a storm like you did this morning, so I think it will have more impact and meaning for you. Remember, you can't stop the storms in life. Some come along that are a result of our own actions so they could have been avoided, but once they occur, you'll need to work through them. They come to test your plans, your will, and your determination. We all have them; it's how we respond to them that'll determine our success."

Alan carefully opened the envelope and began to read:

The Success Grower - Element Six
Storms

Storms are a part of nature. Some can be seen coming from a long distance. Others will appear out of nowhere when least expected.

Storms reveal the measure of a person. They visit the prepared and those who have chosen to let the storms guide them. Success or failure is not determined in the middle of the storm, but by the thought and plans made in advance of any storm forming.

The actions taken in life without a determined plan have the chance to create storms of their own making. These storms are mostly avoidable with careful thought, planning, and concrete goals. Just walking through life is not enough, and these storms will seem to be never-ending.

Even with a well thought-out and considered plan, storms will arise from time to time. Some because it is nature's course. Others will come as a test; a test of the will to persevere, a test of the soundness of plans, and a test of relationships.

As in all things, a choice will be required of you. Will you choose to let the storm destroy your life and plans, or will you choose to build a shelter from the storm and pick up after it is over to keep moving forward? The only way to weather the storm is to go through it.

A tree grows stronger being bent by the wind.

12

Tom was up earlier than usual and fixed a big breakfast of eggs, bacon, and pancakes along with a steaming pot of coffee. Alan was awakened by the commotion and the aroma filling the whole house as if it were a silent alarm clock.

"You're up bright and early," Alan said through a yawn as he pulled out a chair and sat down at the table. "Or I guess it's just early. It's not bright out yet!"

"It's harvest day!" Tom chirped, almost singing it. "This is what it's all about! All the planning and work and attention put into a crop is about to pay off. That's the beauty of farming—you get to plan for and reap a successful harvest each season...if you plan correctly."

"Yes, but then you start all over," Alan pointed out.

"No, that's not accurate," Tom shot back as he flipped a pancake. "If you plan correctly, it's not starting over; it's just a continuation from one harvest to the next. Just because you've reached the goal of a successful harvest doesn't mean you're done. Those are just markers along the way to give you the encouragement to keep going to the next one."

Tom continued, "Take, for instance, the goals you've created for yourself. Is success defined as reaching the goal and then you're done?" Tom waved the spatula at Alan. "If that's what you think, then I haven't done a good enough job teaching you about the purpose of goals. Remember I said when you reach the goal you're working toward, you need to have already planned the next one? That's why I said to set goals for five years from now. As you make progress to those goals, you'll eventually be planning and setting new goals even farther into the future. It's a continual process in order to have a successful life.

"Maybe your goals will change—mine did—and sometimes, the dream changes. When that happens, you sit down and plan new goals to reach the new dream." Tom set a plate of pancakes on the table. Alan could see he had frustrated Tom and had dampened his chipper attitude.

"I really didn't mean it that way, Tom," Alan said. "It just seemed to me that here on the farm, each crop is a new start. I guess it's in the sense that you're starting the path to a new goal for the next crop, but then again it's just a step in the continuation to an ultimate goal. And no disrespect, Tom, but what is the ultimate goal for a farmer? In business, it's building and growing a business to create a product or service that satisfies a need for customers. Then hopefully someday you can either sell the business or retire."

"Ha, ha, you just described farming!" Tom laughed as he put the rest of breakfast on the table. He said, "A farmer's goal is no different. This is his business. His goal is to create a product, the crop that satisfies a need for a customer. Where do you think the flour came from to make these pancakes? You're going to see that product harvested today. And what about the bacon and the eggs, someone had to build and grow a business to produce enough so it's available for everyone. That all started on a farm and became someone's dream.

"And yes, even farmers sometimes look to the day they might sell and retire. But most find it's an enjoyable and rewarding way of life." Tom poured Alan a cup of coffee.

"I really hadn't thought about it that way," Alan said humbly.

"Most people don't. They only see the dirty, hard work and long hours. Success for most farmers isn't measured by the amount of money they make or the things they have, it's the joy and satisfaction of growing, nurturing, and harvesting to help others. And when the storms come, you pick yourself up and keep going."

"I've been thinking about the storms," Alan said. "Here you have your neighbors who have some of the same goals, raising crops and animals. And when the storms come up, it seems everyone goes out to help each other. I don't have that. I probably won't have anyone who understands or even cares about my goals. How can I get the support and help when I need it?" He was feeling alone.

Tom sat down across the table from Alan and put a couple of pancakes on his plate. He said, "I'm glad you have figured that out. Too many times I find individuals who think they can go it alone. I don't know if it's stubbornness or shyness or what. But it's not the best way to succeed. Yeah, you can do it on your own, but I think you need to have an extremely strong and determined personality. Those people are pretty rare. I'll bet if you really look at the way they operate, you'll find they actually had someone to give them advice and guidance. It just wasn't outwardly obvious.

"That's why I told you it's okay to call me if you need to. And I'm glad Cal came by, so you could meet him. You need to have a few people who not only understand the journey you're on and the struggles you face, but who will ask the tough questions and help you see when you're getting off track. Their guidance will make all the difference in the world. We can't do this alone. You can't do this alone. So start now to find others who have achieved similar success, and some who are working on it like you. Just having someone to talk things over will move you farther down the road faster." Tom's tone was encouraging.

"I have some close friends that I could talk to and get their help and advice, I guess," Alan said as he thought about who this might be.

"I would caution you to choose only people who are pursuing their own goals and dreams, or have done so. Friends, and even family, will offer their opinion without any facts or experience to support it, and it may not be helpful. If someone has not gone through their own journey, or isn't going through it to reach goals they have set, their guidance may not and probably will not be beneficial to you. It will most likely dampen your desire to reach your goals."

"So who do I look for, and what real benefit will I get from them?" Alan asked.

"First," Tom said. "Look for people from the profession you work in, but don't only choose them. Then, look at people from other areas of your life, or people you have met in the businesses you have worked with on any of your projects. The one aspect to keep in mind, and this is the most important one, is to pick those that have already achieved the level of success in their lives that you're working toward in your life. If you think that's a bit beyond you right now, then make sure you choose people who are at a success level that's higher than where you are."

"But why would someone like that want to spend time to meet with me and give me advice?" Alan asked, confused.

"Well, they probably already know the benefit of being in a group like this, using the brain power of the group to solve problems, clarify ideas, strengthen their vision, and adjust the path they are on in order to reach their goals.

They most likely will enjoy using the collective knowledge of others in the group who are also at their level of success. You'll get the same insight and advantage, and they'll naturally introduce you to their own network of friends and contacts, which wouldn't have been available to you otherwise," Tom explained as he finished his breakfast.

Alan sat quietly, trying to think about people he could ask to be in this group. After a couple of minutes, Tom broke the silence.

"I'm sure you've heard about this before," Tom said. "It's called a Master Mind group. It was first described in some detail by Napoleon Hill in 1937 in his book, *Think and Grow Rich*.[1] Even Benjamin Franklin created a group like this, and called it a Junto, 'his club of mutual improvement.' If you'll research masterminds, you'll find it has become very popular, and many highly successful people are now either putting together master mind groups or are participating in one. You've heard the saying 'two heads are better than one'? Well, there's a whole lot of truth to that, and if you can have five or six people who can meet together, you'll be amazed at the results everyone in the group will have."

"So how does this group work?" Alan asked. He was now very interested as he poured himself another cup of coffee.

"Well, the actual mechanics of how the group functions varies from group to group. When I was building and growing my business, I asked some of the leading businessmen in the city. I was looking for no more than six who would commit their time to meeting on a regular basis. I chose from different industries: insurance, banking, retail, real estate, manufacturing, and medical. They each had to be highly successful in their business and career, and have the highest integrity. There were both men and women, and over time, some of the participants would change. At first, it was difficult getting them to understand the intent and purpose of the group, and getting their commitment. But once we started meeting, it became clear very quickly the benefit each member of the group was going to have.

"We would meet once a week for at least an hour early in the morning. Each meeting was different, and we would take turns talking about the successes we had in the previous week and any challenges we were working on. Because of the sensitive information, and sometimes very personal information, it was absolutely necessary that each member of the group commit to strict confidentiality. It was a safe place to have serious and personal discussions without the fear of being talked about outside of the group. Sometimes we would spend an entire meeting helping one of the members with an issue, asking pointed and probing questions, questioning motives when they seemed at odds with their goals, giving advice and insight from our own experiences, and encouraging their continued growth toward their success.

"Many of the wealthiest and most successful people in the world have used this valuable practice. They would tell you they owe most of their success, and quicker success, to the benefits they received from participating in a master mind group," Tom explained.

"But why would a successful business person be willing to give some of their time to me?" Alan asked.

"Approach with integrity and sincerity, ask with honesty and respect. Some will refuse, but you'll find those who understand the value of such a group, or have been looking for one themselves but are too busy to put it together. You'll find them grateful for the chance to help others and be helped themselves. Remember, each person in the group needs to be able to benefit from the group. It can't always be give and not receive."

"What if they say no?" Alan felt a bit inadequate.

Tom gathered the breakfast dishes and put them in the sink.

"Oh, some will," he said bluntly. "But that's only one of the tests you'll face on your journey. The question is, will you let that be the reason you quit? If so, you won't be able to face the bigger rejections to come in the future. Everything is a step along the road to your goals. It is the person who persists until he achieves what he wants that reaches his ultimate goal and finds the success he's looking for."

"Okay, I guess I need to start making a list for that too." Alan sighed, and then he finished his coffee.

"Yep, just one more task to add to your plan," Tom said with a laugh. He was washing the dishes. "But for now, we need to head out and see if George has made it to the wheat field yet. It's harvest time, and I think it's the best time of the year!"

The morning humidity was burning off as the sun climbed higher in the sky. Tom and Alan hopped in the pickup and headed over to the wheat field. Alan had no idea what process was involved to harvest wheat, but he could see that Tom was pretty excited about it—he was even walking with a spring in his step.

George was already at the field with some big grain trucks and a couple of harvesters. Alan had seen pictures and video clips of harvesters like these but had never seen one up close.

It was about noon by the time they really got started. Alan heard them talking about moisture content and the wheat being tough. It didn't mean much to him, but he listened with interest, learning as much as he could about a harvest that was so important to Tom. They walked out into the field and took some of the wheat heads, rubbed them between their hands releasing the grain, and blew the chaff away leaving the seed which they promptly popped in their mouth and chewed.

"Alan, you climb up there and ride around with George on the combine." Tom pointed up the steps of the huge machine. "You'll get a great view of the process and how the machine works. And the best part is you can watch the grain pour into the bin in the back. It looks like pure gold to me!"

George climbed the steps and Alan followed. There wasn't a lot of room for both of them in the cab, but Alan found a spot he could sort of sit and watch. There were a lot of switches, levers, and gauges on the right side of where George sat, and a steering wheel and pedals in front of him. Thankfully, there was even air conditioning!

George started it up, let it run for a minute while the big beater reel on the front began to turn, and then headed into the wheat. It was a massive piece of machinery, and it seemed to eat up the wheat as they moved through the field, blowing the dust and remains out the back. George explained to Alan that the front with the rotating reel was called the 'header,' and it had a sickle bar moving back and forth really fast at the bottom, sort of like an electric knife, that cut off the wheat. The reel helped push it into the header. As it moved through the combine, it went through a process that nearly crushed it, similar to rubbing your hands together to release the seed. The seed then fell through small holes in some screens and the rest of it was pushed and blown out the back end. The seed made its way up into the bin in the back.

Alan watched the process with interest and a bit of awe. He looked up into the bin behind him and saw the wheat grain pouring in and quickly filling it.

"This is good wheat!" George said loudly over the noise of the combine. "Tom's getting a good yield this year. He's lucky that storm missed this field; a lot of the other guys weren't as fortunate."

"What do you mean by yield?" Alan asked.

"It's the amount of bushels of seed produced per acre," George explained. "If all the things you planned for happened just right and at the right time—tilling the ground enough to keep the weeds down but not too much to reduce the moisture in the soil, adding fertilizer to the soil when it's needed, planting at the right time, rain at the right time and avoid the storms, then you will end up with a harvest like this one."

"What happens if all of that doesn't work out at the right time?" Alan shouted.

"Well, you might still get a harvest, but it probably won't be anywhere near as good as this. And sometimes it's not even worth the expense of harvesting. You can only control what is in your ability to control," George explained, sounding a little like Tom.

After they rounded the field once, the bin was nearly full. They pulled up alongside the grain truck and unloaded the wheat into the truck. Tom was holding on to the side of the truck, watching the wheat pour in like liquid gold. He had a big grin on his face as the truck began to fill. When the bin was empty, Alan climbed out and George took off to harvest another load.

"Isn't that beautiful?" Tom said excitedly, pointing to the seed in the truck. "This is what it's all about! All the hard work, the time, and the expense. When everything you planned and work so hard for comes together, there's nothing like a big harvest. If you don't plan for a big harvest, you'll never see one."

"But this only took a few months from the time you plowed the soil, planted the seed, got rain at the right time, and survived the storms—all in a few months. How am I supposed to relate this to reaching a harvest of my goals? It'll take years!" Alan said, looking somewhat deflated.

Tom got off the side of the truck and walked over to Alan, put his hands on his shoulders, and looked him in the face.

"Alan, everyone has different goals and a sense of their ultimate dream, or however they might define success for themselves. Remember when you took your ultimate dream of success and then focused on five years into the future? Then you began to break that down into smaller and smaller tasks and goals? When you reach each one of those or accomplish a particular task on the road to your goals, it is a harvest. Some will be bigger than others, but they all should be celebrated just the same.

"For you, it might be getting that important client you've been working on, or it might be the actual completion of a successful marketing campaign. Maybe it's just getting to the point to step out on your own, open up your firm and have a business with your name on it. All of those, and a whole lot more along your journey, are each one a harvest," Tom explained.

Alan was beginning to feel a little better, a little more confident.

Tom continued, "Don't let what you see here with this harvest be a measure of the harvests you'll have. This is very tangible. You can touch it, you can see it as it comes out of the field. But there's a pretty huge cost to get to this point, and as you have seen, some pretty big risks based on the weather that no one can control. Farming is a big gamble, that's why the seasons are important. If I didn't have a plan for what comes next or what to do when the storms come by understanding the seasons, then all of this would have been over a long time ago.

"You need to understand your seasons. The seasons of the career and business you are in, and make plans to adjust or change paths based on the storms or roadblocks that will come up. The person who fails to plan for both the success and the storms has already had their plan determined for them, and that's a life of failure, struggle, mediocrity, and debt. Storm after storm will seem to dominate their life."

At first Alan was sorry he had made the comment about Tom's harvest, but he realized that in just a few short days he'd forgotten the long- and short-term goals he had worked on and was only seeing the effect of this harvest. He was ashamed he had to get this lecture from Tom. He could see the seriousness and concern in Tom's eyes and heard it in his voice.

"I'm sorry I went off about your harvest, Tom," Alan said, looking down at the ground. "I just saw how happy and excited you were about it, and I thought I'd never feel like that. I guess I haven't had the kind of success that I would consider a big harvest. I've signed some big clients over the years and run successful campaigns, but I always saw them as a success for either the client or the firm I worked for. I guess I should celebrate even those, because they were goals that had been achieved."

Tom nodded. "Success and harvest can be found in all areas of our lives. It just depends on how you look at it and plan for it."

"Yeah, well I have a lot of work to do on my plans. I'm worried I'll lose focus and get caught up in my day-to-day life. It's only been a week, and right now, I already feel like I'm forgetting everything."

"You'll get there," Tom said with a light punch to Alan's arm. "This has all been new for you the last week, and I've given you a lot to think about. You've come a long way and it's a process that never ends. If you don't keep refining, adding to, and changing your plans as the times and conditions require, your goals will be more difficult to reach."

After a few more trips around the field, George had the big grain truck filled, and it rolled out of the wheat field to empty the truck at the local grain bin.

"Come on, Alan," Tom motioned. "Hop in the pickup, and we'll follow them. That's the end of the line for the wheat and this harvest, taking it to market."

The county farm Co-op was about five miles down the dusty road. Alan quietly watched the summer farmland slide by as they slowly followed the grain truck. The trip took them past some of the fields that had been destroyed by the storm the day before, and Alan felt a sense of grief and loss for those farmers. It surprised him—he'd never given farming or food production a single thought before, but now, after being here in the middle of it for only a week or so, it felt personal. His eyes started to fill with tears just thinking about all the hard work that went into the crop and how nothing was left now.

"I don't know how you do it," Alan said out loud but not really talking to Tom.

"What's that?" Tom asked.

"Oh, I was just thinking about the storm and the harvest. Here we are with your grain harvest going to market as you said, and we're driving past these other fields that have lost theirs. I feel really sad for them and a bit ashamed that yours wasn't destroyed and you get the benefit of the harvest," Alan said softly.

Tom was silent for a minute, as if looking to find the right words. Finally, he said, "Alan, you can't live your life based on the outcome of someone else's life. If we all did that, nothing would ever get accomplished. We each need to have our own goals and a plan to reach those goals. You know that the weeds and the storms will do everything they can to stop you and derail those plans. You just need to keep your eye on your goal and do your work to get there. You're only responsible for what you can do. Sometimes you will fail, and failure is okay. It's better to try and fail than not try at all, as long as you're learning from it. And yes, at times you will need to help your neighbor when the storms have devastated them."

Tom pointed to the field out Alan's window, and said, "Some of these guys planned for a loss. It won't replace the harvest but it will give them a chance to move on. And some, well, I guess they just want to take the gamble. It'll be hard for them, but at some point, they'll either come up with a new plan or call it quits. If you don't learn from the hard times how to limit the impact in the future—in case it happens again—you certainly won't be successful and reach your goals. Which means, they will remain dreams."

At the Co-op, Alan watched as the truck was weighed so the amount of wheat would be known, before it dumped its load into the grain bin.

Tom explained he would get with the Co-op manager after the harvest was finished and determine the price it would be sold for. That would complete the cycle of this crop—the goal had been achieved. Now his focus would move on to other crops, recover his losses from the storm and the destroyed corn field.

"One successful harvest isn't the end of the road," Tom pointed out. "It's just the accomplishment of that set of goals. A life of success means constantly working to achieve your goals, celebrating when you reach them, and refining them along the way. Success isn't the end result—it's the journey and the process to accomplish your goals."

By evening, George had the entire field harvested and the grain hauled to the Co-op. Tom discussed settling up for the cost of harvesting his wheat with George. Alan just stood there and listened. He didn't understand any of the terms of the payment. They all shook hands, and the trucks and big machines finally rumbled down the road, ready for another day and another wheat field.

Tom looked tired as he and Alan climbed into the pickup for the drive back to the house.

"This was really an interesting day," Alan said, breaking the silence. He wanted to explain what he'd understood so far. "It's been hot and dusty, but I get it now about the harvest. You put in all that time and effort to plow the field and plant the seed, but then you're at the mercy of nature and the rain and storms. When you finally get to the harvest, you remember all the hard work, but now you see the success you worked so hard for. Obviously it doesn't happen by chance.

"If you don't till the soil, it'll be hard and full of weeds. The seed won't plant itself. You need to have a plan. And in this case, that plan is also based on the seasons and time of year."

"I think you've got it now, Alan," Tom said with a tired smile, pushing his cap back a bit on his head. "You won't have anything to harvest without having a plan to get to the harvest. Yes, there'll be things that come up that'll slow you down or completely derail your plans. But overcoming that is also part of the plan. You can't go through life without a plan. If you do, you're only going to get what comes to you, and that may be a whole bunch of junk. If you want to have a successful harvest in your life, even a successful season, you must have a plan. Be committed to your plan, work your plan, always refine your plan, and have people around you who'll support and encourage you."

"It sounds simple when you explain it like that."

"It is simple," Tom added. "But it's not easy. If it was easy, everyone would have success in their life. Well, maybe they do actually. It's been said that 'if you fail to plan, you plan to fail,' so I guess success can be seen in many different ways, huh?"

"Yeah, and I've spent enough of my life without a real concrete plan," Alan acknowledged. "I've just let my life happen. But that's all changed now. I'm excited about my future and the dreams I have for my career and life. I've got a lot of work to do, and I don't know yet how I'll get there, but I now have a plan. Or at least the beginning of a plan."

Tom pulled into the drive of the farmhouse and parked. He was telling Alan how it had been a long and good day for him, for both of them, and how he knew Alan had a vision for his own future. It was reassuring, listening to Tom talk about the others and how excited he was when they'd get to this point, much as he was excited for Alan and what the future had in store for him. Tom also told him how hard it was going to be. This was just the beginning, his work with Alan was now really about to start, and Alan felt grateful once again that here was someone who was happy and willing to help him.

After they got cleaned up from the hot and dirty day of harvest, and had dinner, Tom handed Alan another envelope. This one said 'The Success Grower - Element Seven.'

The Success Grower - Element Seven
Harvest

A harvest is merely a marker. It is not and should not be the singular aim of your efforts. It is a guidepost, a scorecard, a tally sheet of the actions taken in achieving your goals.

A harvest is necessary for success; otherwise, the path becomes meaningless and lonely on which there is only frustration and defeat. At the end of each accomplishment comes the chance to celebrate and bring in the fruits of your labor. Take time to count your harvest—the success you have achieved—and look back at the journey you took to arrive at this place. See the struggles, see the times you were unsure, and see the people who helped along the way.

A harvest isn't accomplished alone. Celebrate with those who walked with you on this journey. Celebrate along the way. Giving encouragement to others will yield an even larger harvest.

A harvest isn't the end of the journey, it is only a tally of the success you have had. At times it will be large, other times rather small. In every success reap the harvest it offers in order to grow larger in the next one.

A harvest is a time to gather your resources. The saying goes, "Don't eat your seed wheat." At each harvest, put aside enough resources in order to have plenty for the next season or next goal. If you lose it all or use it up at each harvest, no future growth is possible. At each successful harvest you should be planning for the next one, and the one after that, and the one after that...

Achieving the goals you have planned and worked hard for will yield the results of your efforts. Enjoy the harvest, but don't linger long. An even greater harvest is waiting.

*Grab **your FREE copy** (retail value of $147) of all eight Elements including a template designed to guide your growth to success, visit: **TheSuccessGrower.com/Elements** (no credit card required).*

13

Alan felt tired and exhausted when he got up the next morning. The sun was a bit higher in the sky this time, which meant he had slept in and Tom had left him alone. He found the coffee pot still on with a bit of strong coffee left, so he finished it and made himself some toast with butter and jelly. The house was quiet, and with the strong coffee in the pot he figured Tom had already started his day a few hours ago.

He got dressed and headed out to see what Tom was up to. The wheat harvest was finished, and the corn, well, it couldn't even be called corn anymore, needed to be plowed up according to Tom. So there was plenty of work to be done.

Alan heard the tractor start up, so he followed the sound and found Tom sitting in the tractor which was hooked up to another large piece of equipment.

"Morning, sunshine!" Tom yelled over the noise of the tractor as Alan walked up.

"What are you doing?" Alan yelled back.

Tom climbed out of the tractor so they wouldn't need to yell.

"Now that we've harvested the wheat, the field needs to be plowed to break up the soil that's been untouched for the last eight or nine months and start the process for the next crop. The weeds will start growing quickly since they're now exposed to the sunlight," Tom explained. "I want you to bring the pickup and follow me over there. Today you get to learn to drive a tractor and plow a field!" Tom slapped Alan on the arm.

"Uh, well I'm not sure I'm ready for that," Alan said hesitantly.

"Sure you are!" Tom climbed back on the tractor. "Just follow me over there."

Tom drove the tractor and the plow hooked to it out of the yard, and headed down to the wheat field that had just been harvested the day before. Alan followed in the pickup as they slowly made their way down the road.

It took about fifteen minutes to get there, and then Tom slowed and turned into the field. He stopped and got off, and told Alan to park the pickup in the corner of the field.

"I'll get it started and make sure it's plowing deep enough and set right. I'm going to go around the outside edge and make my way back here. I'll pick you up when I get back," Tom explained.

Alan got out and watched as Tom set the plow and took off. The tractor was really loud and the dust boiled up from the ground. This was obviously going be a really dusty job. As Tom got to the far end of the field, it became quiet. Alan could only hear the breeze blowing and a few birds. It was really peaceful out here, far away from traffic and city noise, Alan realized. He was actually going to miss it and he suddenly felt sad.

Tom brought the tractor back to where Alan was waiting. He stopped, hollered at Alan to climb in the cab with him, and took off again. This time around Tom explained how to go and stop, the speed needed to go, and how to watch where he plowed, following the previous path so that he overlapped a bit with the plow. Corners needed a little planning and timing so you didn't make a loop.

Tom stopped, let Alan sit in the seat, and they took off again. Alan was scared and thrilled at the same time, keeping a death grip on the steering wheel. He had never driven anything so big and powerful. He was afraid he'd mess something up or tear something up. Tom assured him he'd be fine and rode along for a couple more rounds.

Alan gripped the steering wheel so hard his hands started to cramp, and fear took hold of him at each corner. Eventually it got a little easier.

"See, I told you it wouldn't be difficult," Tom said loudly over the noise of the tractor. "Every new job or task is at first frightening and you're not sure you can do it, or do it well. The best plan is to learn what you need to know then jump right in and start. Thinking about it for too long will make it seem much harder than it really is, and then ol' procrastination will show up."

"I certainly don't want to break something or tear it up," Alan yelled back as he intently focused on his previous path.

"I wouldn't like that either. But sometimes that comes with doing new tasks," Tom said. "So you need to prepare as well as you can. If it's a big step or task, make sure you have someone to teach you what you need to learn or to guide you along the way."

"Like you and Cal on this new success path you've helped me see?" Alan asked.

"Exactly like that. There'll be many opportunities for you to grow personally and professionally, and it's wise to have others to help guide you and be there for insight and wisdom. When you reach a roadblock, or as in this case, a corner—" Tom pointed, reminding Alan to turn. "—it will make your decisions easier when you have counsel from others who've had similar experiences."

Tom added, "Now stop after you turn this next corner and let me off. You'll be good until lunch in a couple of hours, and then we'll swap."

"You're going to leave me?" Alan shot back now really scared, his eyes as wide as saucers.

"Yep, you're doing great! Just keep following the path before and overlap a bit, you'll be fine."

Tom went to sit in the pickup, saying something about taking a nap. Alan, scared but determined, started off around the field again. It was a huge responsibility to handle such a large piece of machinery, knowing that it was on him now to make sure the field was plowed properly. Eventually, with each succeeding corner, it became easier and Alan relaxed a bit more.

As he worked his way around the field, he could see his progress. It was slow and minimal at first, but soon the edge of the field got farther away. He didn't always keep the rows real straight, and sometimes, he overlapped way more than he needed. It was obvious how crooked he went at times. Then he figured out how he could watch in the distance ahead of him and plan for more or less overlap in order to straighten his path out again.

Alan thought about his new journey for his life and future success. He compared it to this field he was plowing. To start anew would be frightening and hard, and he would need to learn new skills. He figured he won't be real good at it at first, and he'd need someone to help show him how to get started and point out the corners.

Just like he figured out how to make adjustments and straighten out his path from his previous trip around the field, he realized the more he followed his plan and took action to reach his goals, the more it would get easier. He'd have to make fewer adjustments, or at least fewer big adjustments. What he needed to be sure of was that he had good guides and teachers along the way.

Around noon Tom came driving out into the field. Alan had made great progress, and Tom looked grateful for the help. He motioned for Alan to stop, and he showed him how to shut off the tractor. Alan was exhausted from the tension, the bumpy ride, and the heat. He never gave a thought to how hard driving a tractor could be.

"Hop off," Tom said. "I brought some sandwiches and iced tea. We'll sit in the pickup and have lunch, and then I'll take over for a while."

They sat with the windows down to let the breeze blow through while they ate the lunch Tom had made. Alan was tired and grateful for the chance to sit still.

"Tell me what you learned out there today, Alan," Tom said, taking a drink of his iced tea.

"I was really scared at first. I was afraid I would mess up or break something. The corners were hard to time right and some of them are pretty messed up. It was really difficult to watch ahead to make sure I was going in the right direction, and watch the plow behind to make sure it was overlapped enough. I finally figured out how to judge the distance with the frame of the window, so I didn't need to look back so much."

Tom, seemingly impressed, nodded in approval.

Alan continued, "And once I focused more on where I was going, I could see how crooked I'd been the last time around and realized I could overlap more in some places and less in others and straighten it out."

"Well done!" Tom said, slapping him on the leg. "You picked that up pretty fast on your own because I didn't tell you any of that."

"Yeah, you pretty much said 'this is how you go, this is how you stop, keep that overlapped back there,' and then you left me!" Alan laughed.

"The best way to learn is to do," Tom said. "You can waste your time being shown how or reading about it. But until you do, it you really don't learn anything."

"I learned I don't really want to be a farmer." Alan chuckled. "But I did realize I'll struggle at first while working on my new goals. There'll be processes and rules and expectations I haven't even thought about that will come up. I will need to face them head on, maybe one at a time, and make sure I have people I can go to who have the experience I can learn from."

Tom smiled and looked out his window as Alan talked. Their time together was almost over, and although it was invigorating to see Alan come this far and be excited about his future, he was going to miss him. The beginning of a new journey toward a goal you have determined for your own life is thrilling at first, but he knew the hard times will come. That made him sad, but he knew Alan was going to need to go through them. He was confident Alan would make it through. He could see in Alan the determination and the belief in himself that were extremely important for success.

"With time and experience it gets a bit easier," Alan continued.

"Yes it does," Tom replied. "But there will always be a new challenge or roadblock, and you'll need to make sure you have a good team of people around you and others you can turn to for advice and knowledge. We can't do this alone, we were never expected to." Tom turned to Alan. "Let me ask you something. Do you think you could now teach someone how to drive that tractor and plow the field?"

"Well, to a point, yes. I'm sure there are a lot of things about it I don't know yet," Alan admitted.

"But what you do know, do you think you could teach that?" Tom asked.

"Sure," Alan said confidently. "I could do that."

"Good," Tom said, looking intently at Alan. "That's the biggest key to success. Teach what you learn. Someone else is coming behind you who'll need to learn what you know. Success in life isn't about what we do or what we accomplish, it's about helping others get what they want."

"Well, I don't know if anyone will be needing my advice on how to drive a tractor," Alan joked.

"Okay, maybe not," Tom said, rolling his eyes. "You might be surprised some day. What I'm saying is, we have a responsibility to pass on what we've learned and help others find their way on their own journey. You've heard the adage, 'A rising tide lifts all boats,' and it's true. The more you help others, the more success you find in your own life."

"That's what you've been doing this past week, I guess. Isn't it?" Alan asked humbly.

"Yes. I teach what I know. I use the tools of my knowledge and my trade to teach practical lessons for others to succeed in their life. I'm not teaching you how to grow crops and farm, I'm teaching you how to grow the success of the crops you choose to plant. The elements of success are the same no matter what you apply them to. Sometimes it's easier to learn here, because the cycle from plowing to planting to cultivating to harvesting is rather quick and the lessons can be more obvious. Also, the storms can be instantly devastating. You were lucky enough to experience most of it," Tom pointed out.

"So we're finished?" Alan asked, his voice sad.

"Yes, you've come a long way in the past week," Tom replied. "I went in to town and checked on your car with Buddy. He's almost done, and you'll be able to pick it up tomorrow. I figured you'd be leaving then."

"Oh, okay, thanks for checking on it." Alan had a sinking feeling in his stomach. "I guess I need to start getting my things together tonight."

"There's one last thing." Tom pulled another envelope from the dash of the pickup. "It's the last one. Probably the most important one. It's the key to your success and how quick you get there. We talked about this quite a bit yesterday."

Tom handed Alan the envelope. It said on the front: 'The Success Grower - Element Eight.'

"I'll go drive the tractor for a while," Tom said, suddenly getting out of the pickup. "If you want to run into town or whatever, go ahead. I'll see you back at the house later this afternoon, after I finish here."

Tom quickly walked off toward the tractor with tears in his eyes. He always hated this part.

The Success Grower - Element Eight
Mentor & Mastermind

No one is successful alone. The path to success is varied and full of obstacles that will test your will, your desire, and your determination. It is also scattered with temptations of ease, quick success, and praise.

In all of time, great success has come to those who seek out the wisdom of those who have travelled the path of success before them. To pass on the knowledge of maneuvering through obstacles and challenges in order to help another reach their goal is the ultimate achievement of success.

Seek out a mentor, a guide, who has traveled a similar path and is an expert in your endeavor. Their counsel should be firm, not self-serving. They will help you see the "what if" of your situation and have strong expectations for their continued commitment.

Identify the kind of person who has the experience you need to reach your goals. Ask them to meet with you. Let them know what help you are needing and why you are looking for a mentor. You will find the right one at the right time. As you grow in your abilities and needs, move on to another.

A person who has achieved success enjoys sharing their journey and knowledge with others. Wisdom is only useful when passed on. Cherish this person and this relationship.

Connect with others who are of the same mind and on a similar journey for success. Choose those who now are where you are aiming to be in life and in your endeavors. In any endeavor, relationships are key to your success, and the support of others will help carry you through hard times.

A *mastermind* is a select group of fellow travelers seeking success in their own way. To try it on your own will be like walking in a twisting canyon with steep, high walls on both sides. Progress will be seen, but obstacles will appear suddenly and will seem impassable.

A mastermind can see from above. They do not walk your exact path, and many have travelled a similar canyon. They see from experience and have gained knowledge useful for others. They question your decisions and test your vision, your planning and determination. They gently, or at times forcefully, help correct your course. They compel you to clarify and define your problems. They are your strongest champions.

Being part of a mastermind brings with it the responsibility to help other members in their quest for success. While contemplating the advice you might give to another, it most frequently reveals the solution you have been seeking for in a similar obstacle, but you just have been too blind to see it.

At all times, a mastermind must operate with trust and truth. In confidence is found trust. In truth is found encouragement and wisdom. Support of each of the individuals in a mastermind is the key to success. The whole is greater than the sum of its parts.

The journey will seem lonely. Surround yourself with like-minded travelers. Lift up, hold up, and be lifted up. Success is just ahead.

14

Alan went to check on his car. Buddy was busily working underneath another pickup and slid out as Alan walked up.

"Alan, I'm glad you're here," Buddy said, wiping oil from his hands. "I've got your car all done and she runs great! Those foreign cars are tricky, especially with the tranny, but it's all fixed. I even changed your oil and stuff, no charge, since it looked like it had been a while and needed it."

"Thanks, Buddy, I appreciate that! I've been dreading this moment, but I did put myself in this situation so let's get it over with. How much is it costing me?"

"Well, the transmission for these cars aren't cheap and there's the time to replace it. I don't fudge on my time or throw extras in to run up the bill, but it's pricey."

"Okay, I get it," Alan said, crossing his arms in frustration. "Just tell me and let's get it over with."

Buddy walked into his office with Alan following close behind. He picked up some papers from his desk and handed them to Alan.

Alan took the papers and looked at the list of parts and labor charge. He held his breath as he turned the page. When he got to the bottom, he was left speechless. It said, "Paid in Full."

"What's this all about?" Alan managed to ask when he was able to speak again.

Buddy face broke out in a huge grin, not holding it in any longer.

"Tom was in this morning and took care of it," Buddy said. "He said to tell you it was now your responsibility to help someone else in need. He's a great man. I've learned so much from him over the last few years. I wouldn't be here with this shop and my own business if it wasn't for him. I was lost, frustrated, and wanted something I could call my own. My time with Tom was the turning point in my life. I didn't want anything big, I just wanted it to be my own and something I loved doing. I have a great life and can raise my family in this little town of wonderful people."

Alan couldn't hold back the tears now. He didn't know what to say, he stood there staring at Buddy, tears streaming down his face.

"I, I don't have any words," Alan stammered.

"I know." Buddy put his hand on Alan's shoulder. "I know how you feel. Tom has a way of pouring himself into people who are searching. He finds them occasionally, or maybe I should say they're sent to him, and teaches them his wisdom of the ages. It's nothing new, he just has a way of making it clear."

"Yeah, he does," Alan said, sitting down in a chair. "He's a very kind and patient teacher. I've heard of some of his 'Elements' before but never put them together in the way he does. It's a very effective approach."

"I don't know what your path and plans are, Alan," Buddy said. "But I do know that if you put the Elements to work in your life every day, you'll reach the goals you have. My dream was a simple life with my own business, treating people with respect and honesty, and raising a family around close friends. I found it here. And you'll find your dream if you keep looking and working on your plan."

"I still don't know what to say, Buddy." Alan quietly wiped the tears from his face.

"Just say *thank you,* and go make your own success-ful future. That's all he wants for you," Buddy said. They headed back into the shop, Buddy tossing the car keys to Alan. "Here's your keys, the car's around back. Keep your eyes on the road, and come back and see us when you get a chance."

"I sure will, Buddy. Thanks for your help and your work. I know where to find a good mechanic now. I'll be in tomorrow to get the car since I have Tom's truck right now."

Buddy disappeared underneath the truck he was work-ing on earlier. Alan got into Tom's pickup and headed back to the farm.

Alan couldn't believe Tom had paid for his car repairs. He certainly didn't need to do that, and it made Alan a bit uncomfortable and embarrassed. How would he be able to make it up to him? He slowly drove back to the farm, taking in the peacefulness of the countryside.

Tom came back from the field, parked the tractor by the shop, and slowly walked to the house. He was tired and dirty, and he knew another chapter was about to close in his life. He thought about the past week and how much Alan had learned and changed. He loved the time he got to spend teaching his insight and knowledge for living a successful life. He just always hoped it stuck, and that the lessons will be passed on to others.

His time was growing shorter and there were many more who needed to be able to see there's hope for their future.

He had taught several, and now it was their turn to pass it on as they also continued to grow in their knowledge and abilities.

Alan was waiting for him, sitting at the kitchen table with a big glass of iced tea. He was swirling his glass, not looking at Tom. "You didn't need to do that," Alan said.

"You're right, I didn't. But I wanted to do it."

"Why? I'm the one who owes you. You put me up for over a week and fed me, I sure owe you for that!" There was a touch of anger in Alan's voice.

"Nope, that was the right thing to do. There wasn't anywhere else for you to stay anyway. Besides, you hoed some weeds, mowed the grass, and drove the tractor for me!" Tom offered.

"I certainly didn't do those well enough for you to pay for my car repairs."

Tom poured a glass of tea and sat down at the table. He said, "Alan, it's a gift from me to you. You're about to start on a journey that will demand a lot of resources. It'll cost you a lot of time, money, and emotional resources. Some days will seem to be a breeze, and other days it'll appear as if the whole world is working against you. When those days come, I want you to remember the gift."

"Why, because it will make me feel better?" Alan asked stiffly.

"No, because when those days come, I want you to find someone you can give a gift to," Tom calmly suggested.

"What kind of gift? I won't be able to spend that kind of money!"

"It doesn't always need to be money or that much. But you never know, at some point it could be even more." Tom smiled. "Just remember, you won't succeed on your journey to your goals and dreams if your focus is always on what you want and what you're doing. There are people in the world who'll cross your path for a reason. Some are there to help you and some are there for you to help. The only true measure of success I've found is how many people I can help who have a need I can fill. The rest of it is just a means to be able to help them."

"So you're saying that while I'm working to build and grow my business and life plans, I need to look for people to help? Won't that cause me to lose focus?" Alan asked, his tone confused.

"You don't need to actively look for people to help, although that in itself is a worthy path to take. I'm saying you need to have in your heart the awareness of people in need, and if you're in a position to help them you should. It'll be part of the testing on your journey. If you only work for your own gain and purposes, you'll certainly lose in the end. I've seen many people create great wealth and businesses who were only interested in what they could get or how much they could accumulate. In the end, they either lost it all or spent a life of loneliness, and ended up destroying themselves."

"I don't want to do that," Alan agreed. "I've already kind of done that."

"Living for yourself is great for a while, but you'll end up living a lonely and unfulfilled life. Now that you have a plan you're committed to, add one more component to it. As they say, 'find a need and fill it.' Well, I have found a quicker way to succeed and that is to find that need on a personal level and fill it. The rest of your plan will be much simpler. Focus more on serving others than on serving your-self or your plan."

Alan sat quietly, staring into his glass of iced tea and think-ing about the past week and how much Tom had given to him. He could see now that Tom was giving him much more than he could ever give back. In fact, the amount of money he spent to pay his repair bill seemed insignificant compared to the gift of knowledge and counsel he'd received since coming here. He sensed Tom's life was a bit fuller now that he'd given away his gift again. *There must be something to it*, Alan thought.

"All right," Alan said. "I think I get it. I owe you more than I can ever repay, but I think the best way is for me to pass it on to someone else. You've poured yourself into me, and you didn't come looking for me. Our paths crossed, and I had a need you could fill."

"I think you get it now," Tom said with a smile and a yawn. "I'm tired so I'm going to bed. I'll see you in the morning, and we'll go get your car. Sleep well."

Tom got up and headed off to bed. Alan sat for a while longer, thinking about all the things that happened since he ran off the road. His life was on cruise control, and he wasn't really focused on his future. And because of that, when the only plan he had was changed by his boss, he blew up and left. Now he realized it was because he wasn't in control of his future and actually didn't have a plan that he was committed to for the future. He was just letting his life happen.

That wasn't going to be the case from now on. He had a plan, and he was committed to following it. His future career, life, and happiness depended on it.

He could never repay Tom, but he will always be grateful to him.

15

Alan didn't sleep well and was up early before Tom. He made a pot of coffee, poured a cup, and headed outside to watch the sun come up. It wasn't a sight you saw very often in the city, and he was amazed with the beauty of the day waking up. Birds were just beginning to start their morning songs and the dew had already made its appearance, forming droplets along each blade of grass. Alan sat on the steps to the house, taking it in one last time.

Tom came out with his cup of coffee in hand and sat next to Alan without saying a word. Neither one could find the words to begin the goodbye process, so they stayed silent and watched their corner of the world wake up.

The sun was instantly warming their faces; it was going to be another hot day.

"How about we head into town and get breakfast at the Sunrise Café?" Tom said as he slowly stood up and stretched. "You want one of those cinnamon rolls before you leave?"

"Sure, for old time's sake, huh?" Alan tried to sound cheerful.

Alan gathered up the little clothes he had with him and threw them in his bag. He tossed it in the back of the pickup and they started off to town.

Alan quietly watched the countryside go by, thinking about all that had happened since he first made the trip to Tom's house. A man he only met not more than ten days ago, and yet, now found it difficult to leave.

He felt a sense of excitement and fear at the same time. Tom had given him something valuable and helped him see that whatever he wanted to accomplish in life was up to him and not someone else. He just needed to commit to his plan, believe in himself, and never give up. He knew it wouldn't be easy and he wished he lived closer to Tom for his guidance.

He had the Elements of success Tom had given him, and now it was up to him to complete the path he would take. Thankful for the drive home, he had a lot of work and planning to do and he was determined to do it.

After having another one of Evelyn's heavenly cinnamon rolls and saying goodbye, they walked the two blocks to Buddy's shop without saying a word. They retrieved Alan's car. Alan tossed his bag into the trunk and turned to face Tom.

"I don't know what to say, other than 'Thank You,' and that doesn't really get it." Alan had tears in his eyes. "You have given me a gift far greater than I'll ever be able to repay. I won't ever forget this, and I certainly won't let you down."

"It's not me you'd be letting down, it's you," Tom said, gently tapping Alan's chest. "I'm just the messenger and guide; it's your life and dreams. You know how to go after them now, so if you don't, you're only letting yourself down. I've done my part, you go and do yours. Believe in yourself, do the work, and you'll find that others will believe in you too."

A handshake turned into a quick hug. Alan got into his car, turned the key, and started off on his new life.

ACKNOWLEDGEMENTS

I WOULD LIKE TO THANK LINDA, MY WIFE, for the patience in allowing me to explore my own growth journey and all the time I spent with my nose in a book working on my own self-esteem and personal development; Craig, my son, for his insight and honest input into the form this book should take; Chad Ingram for his support and endless encouragement to just write and his weekly accountability; my dad, Clyde Schinnerer, for his patient endurance and teaching a teenager about farming and being a grower of people; Kary Oberbrunner and this Author Academy Elite team for always being available and supportive. Thanks to Precy Larkins for her editing and proofreading skills. Much appreciation to Lizaa for her patience and the time she took with the cover design.

Special thanks go to Amy Calderon, Julie Chester, Jessie Bryant and the unnamed draft readers who gave valuable feedback and the encouragement to continue writing. And finally, a very special thanks to Glenda Schinnerer, my mother, for her never-ending support and belief in me.

NOTES

1. Hill, Napoleon. *Think and Grow Rich*. Cleveland, Ohio: The Ralston Publishing Co. 1937

2. Allen, James. *As A Man Thinketh*. United States. 1903

3. Carnegie, Dale. *How to Win Friends and Influence People*. New York, NY: Simon and Schuster. 1936

4. Proverbs 23:7, KJV

5. Proverbs 4:23, 25-26 NIV

6. 1 Corinthians 15:36 NIV

Mark Schinnerer is a grower. Through his speaking, coaching, facilitating and writing, he helps individuals and organizations identify their strengths, their goals, and their motivation for achieving them.

Mark has worked on his own personal growth journey ever since he left the farm and went to college. He has always worked to be encouraging and helpful for others and to find ways to make them or their projects successful. Today, his growth journey has led him to investing in the dreams and goals of others so they can live a life of fulfillment and achievement. He is the founder of *The Success Grower*, which serves individuals seeking to grow their own successful life.

An avid gardener, he finds joy in the soil and the bounty it produces. He and his wife, Linda, are blessed with three wonderful children and six amazing grandchildren.

Connect at: MarkSchinnerer.com

PLANT THE SEED
WORKSHOP

Identify your goals and dreams to achieve
the success you have always wanted.

Plant The Seed workshop guides you to develop
your individual plan for growth and
reaching your goals and dreams.

Let us help you harvest your dreams.

Our *Plant The Seed* workshops can be accessed
in an online version or an in-person workshop.

If you're interested in reaching the success
you have only dreamed about,
we have a *Plant The Seed* workshop that is right for you.

Visit

THESUCCESSGROWER.COM

YOUR NEXT STEP

Join a Success Grower Coaching Circle

Author Mark Schinnerer will walk you through a process to cultivate your dreams into goals so that you can plant seeds of success and reap the harvest of your potential.

You can have what you secretly dream about by writing it down and speaking it into existence.

Find the fulfillment many others have found while participating in this productive experience. No matter where you are in the world, you can be in the circle with a field of growers.

Find out more at

THESUCCESSGROWER.COM/CIRCLE

What harvest are you giving up by not becoming your own SUCCESS GROWER?

INVITE MARK INTO
Your Organization or Business

Author – Speaker – Coach

Mark understands how important it is to pick a speaker who understands what results you are looking for and actually works to make it happen. Mark's personal style and approach, along with his unique framework, sets him apart as an ideal choice for a lot of organizations and businesses. Each message is individualized for his clients so they can achieve a successful outcome.

Contact Mark today to start planting seeds of success.

MARKSCHINNERER.COM

CPSIA information can be obtained
at www.ICGtesting.com
Printed in the USA
FFOW04n0456271117
43699680-42545FF